Denise Danks  teacher, but d
rooms and the
very early on. Unemployed and in desperate need of a free lunch, she began her career in journalism in 1977 and specialized in writing about information technology for most of it. She has written about computers and the computer industry for almost every major specialist publication, as well as for women's magazines and the national press. She was a trainee reporter on The *West Briton* in Truro, Cornwall, a county her family moved to from Singapore when she was eleven. After returning to London to work on computer magazines, she eventually became the managing director of a technology news agency before going freelance in 1987 in order to spend more time with her daughter, Alexandra. In 1988, she won the LBC Conversationalist of the Year award. Denise, who has a Greek mother and an English father, has one brother, a half-sister, and is married to a rather nice computer engineer.

The Pizza House Crash

DENISE DANKS

Futura

A Futura Book

First published in Great Britain in 1989 by
Futura Publications, a Division of
Macdonald & Co (Publishers) Ltd
London & Sydney

The author is grateful to Methuen Publishers, London for permission to
quote from THE THREEPENNY OPERA by Berthold Brecht, published in
1973 by Eyre Methuen, London.

ISBN 0 7088 4374 3

Typeset by Selectmove Ltd, London
Reproduced, printed and bound in Great Britain by
BPCC Hazell Books Ltd
Member of BPCC Ltd
Aylesbury, Bucks, England

Futura Publications
A Division of
Macdonald & Co (Publishers) Ltd
Orbit House
1 New Fetter Lane
London EC4A 1AR
A member of Maxwell Macmillan Pergamon Publishing Corporation

To my husband Nicky
and our beautiful daughter,
Alexandra Ourania

Acknowledgements

My sincere thanks to my husband Nicky for helping with the idea, my agent Gloria Ferris for being big-hearted, my friends and associates: Mike Penny, Paul Reason, Robert Schifreen, Barbara Ellis, Adam Page, John Conway for helping with the technical stuff, and Enid Blyton, without whom none of this would have been possible.

CHAPTER ONE

I HEARD ABOUT THE DEATH of my cousin Julian from an inebriated headhunter – the executive sort, of course. When he told me, neither of us realised I was related to the deviant corpse which had bequeathed as rich a piece of gossip as either of us had ever heard.

"Fifty grand," Barnaby had wailed, *sotto voce*. He was brimming with Remy Martin and the best part of two bottles of Chablis. I wasn't far behind him, I have to admit, and was feeling it. That's the trouble with nouvelle cuisine: the drink hits your stomach lining before the food does. Still, I like to take advantage of free lunches in Mayfair restaurants when they come my way.

"Fifty grand, the merest weekend away," – more soft and pathetic wails from my host, who was becoming horribly theatrical. One arm hung limply over the back of his handsome ebony chair, and the other dragged a black Sobranie from his petulant mouth. His hair was fashionably short at the sides, with an asymmetrical wave on top. His fine navy striped suit was immaculately cut but his red silk tie had loosened a little, giving him an insouciant air of 'Eighties City decadence. Nevertheless, I thought he looked quite fetching – certainly more fetching than I did, but then he could afford to. It was hard to keep up with the Barnabys of this world on a journalist's pay, and my black, sartorially safe, creative-media look was rapidly fading into shabbiness.

While he groaned on, I tried to work out whether my two-dimensional dessert would spring up into 3-D, like a pop-up picture book. I picked and teased at the razor-fine, translucent raspberry slices set in a delicate film of lilac jelly. My absorption with it irritated Barnaby a little.

1

"Did you hear what I said?" he demanded, slurring slightly.

"Yes," I said, finally popping a slither of fruit in my mouth, which – hardly being full – allowed me to continue, "you said fifty grand, twice."

"We lost fifty thousand pounds, and what is more, we lost it on a bloody perv – a bloody ridiculous perv at that."

I waited. It would be interesting to discover what in the world Barnaby Page found perverse. He looked from side to side, more for effect than for confidentiality, and leant towards me until our noses were separated by the two frail fuchsias in the centre of the tiny oval table.

"You are not going to believe this," he whispered, pausing to drain his brandy glass and run his perfect pink tongue over his rosy lips. "I set up this amazing deal to take a totally talentless programmer to a California start-up – five-figure salary, profit share, car, fast European, of course, relocation expenses – the whole doggy-bag, my dear. You name it he was going to get it."

I waved the choking fumes of his Sobranie away from my face. Barnaby joined in for a second by flapping his elegant hands about.

"Sorry. . . anyway, we were all set to go for next week, when the witless prole hangs himself and sours the whole deal!"

He stubbed his cigarette out in my plate with considerable feeling, then turned and ordered more brandy. The waiter hurried over. I pushed my plate away and covered my glass.

"Sure?" said Barnaby, indicating a double for himself.

"Sure, no thanks. I'll have some coffee now." I looked up at the dark, curly-haired waiter and smiled graciously.

In a minute the waiter returned, poured coffee, and distributed some soft sugary pastel-coloured bonbons. Then Barnaby began again, this time with a snorting chortle.

"You are not going to believe this," he said, shaking his head.

"Barnaby, get on with it," I groaned.

"It wasn't an ordinary hanging. It had a certain . . .

panache, shall we say? He didn't hang himself as in *hang* himself." He helpfully mimed a rope around his neck and tugged upwards with his red silk tie. "He was found winched up in some harness, hanging from the ceiling, handcuffed, stark bloody naked except for some overtight Janet Raeger's and a cute rubber mask!"

Barnaby was snorting heavily with amusement by then, but I was a bit puzzled. With feigned exasperation but genuine enjoyment, he leaned forward again and whispered to me.

"He suffocated in the rubber mask. . . you know. . . while he was cli-max-ing." Barnaby mouthed the syllables for me. "It was an accident that it went too far. . ."

"Oh, that's awful," I said with very little depth of feeling. After all, it was a ridiculous way to die.

"Yes, isn't it? But not half as awful as losing my commission, I can tell you. Fifty thousand pounds! Jesus H! I mean, why couldn't he wait until he got out there?"

This was no halfhearted heartlessness. Barnaby meant it.

"Perhaps he wanted to celebrate, you know, the new job and all that," I volunteered, and Barnaby gave me a bitter smile. I thought I might draw a little more out of the story, so I asked him how come they had managed to select a programmer with no talent and a weird sex life?

"God knows. We had better people on our books, but after all the interviews, they still chose him."

"What sort of firm, Barnaby?"

"Little software house, set for high growth in lifestyle programs. Very Californian – programs to help you lose weight, work hard, love your fellow man, find inner peace, all that sort of crap."

"And who was he?"

Barnaby waggled a finely manicured finger at me. "This is not for publication. Georgina. The tip for the start-up you can have, if it's of any use, but the corpse stays buried. OK?"

"You mean, no 'kinky sex kills computer boffin' stories? Oh, please!" I tried to look miffed, and then it occurred to me: how come the locals hadn't strung the tale to Fleet Street?

"Barnaby, how come the. . ."

He cut me short with a vulpine smile and rubbed his thumb over his fore and middle fingers.

"Lots of crisp ones, my dear. We don't want the whole world to know, do we? It's not good for business. Clients don't want to know that our three-tiered interviews and pyschological scanning techniques can't pick out the morally unsound."

I paused to consider why he hadn't offered me lots of crisp ones. In fact no bribe at all. Or was this it, designer lunch for two and a tip for a down-page filler? He couldn't be relying on our friendship: that was so unlike him.

"OK, just out of interest then, who was he?"

"One Julian Kirren."

The tiny coffee cup fell from my hands and cracked onto the table, splintering its shell-shaped saucer and scattering little shards of china in all directions.

The waiter appeared instantly, to cast a cloth like a shroud over the broken mess and to allay what he imagined was my concern for the establishment's crockery.

"Barnaby," I said weakly, "I think I need some air."

CHAPTER TWO

I DECIDED, UNDER THE CIRCUMSTANCES, not to return to the office, but instead to go home. Despite his condition, Barnaby managed to hail a cab, whose unusually taciturn driver advised me of his right not to transport me "more than six miles out". My humble housing association flat in Bow was "not in Central London, mate", and if it wasn't for Barnaby's prestidigitatorial flourish of a twenty-pound note, we would have been left swaying on the pavement in a fug of diesel fumes. I protested at his extravagance and the cabbie's bloodless capitalism, but suddenly it began to rain, and my outrage succumbed at the first heavy drops splashing down on the beetle blackness of the cab's bonnet. I climbed in with a great show of reluctance and looked appreciatively out of the window at Barnaby, whose glum, dissolute face bore witness to the fact that his only hope of now getting home rested with London Regional Transport.

There were four messages on my telephone answering machine when I got home half an hour later. My editor, Max Winter, had left a terse enquiry as to my whereabouts; Julian's sister, my cousin Anne, had recorded a tense and tearful invitation to his funeral the next day; my solicitor stated politely that he couldn't trace my errant husband, Eddie Powers, in order to serve him the divorce papers; and the aforementioned Eddie had left a short, slurred message that he needed to see me, but he didn't say why.

It was 4.30pm on a Wednesday afternoon, the day before *Technology Week* went to press, and I should certainly have been at my desk. The pressure would be building for front-page stories that would underline the paper's reputation as the top computer industry weekly in the country. Its team of reporters would be making up for at least three days of apparent indolence as imminent deadlines lashed them into consciousness. I had accepted Barnaby's invitation for lunch in the confidence that I had at least two stories, maybe three, that could be pumped out on Thursday provided I worked late that Wednesday evening. Now the situation was different. I was at home, feeling tired, upset, unsteady and dehydrated, and tomorrow I had a funeral to go to.

There was some grapefruit juice and a bottle of soda water in the fridge. I mixed some in a glass and drank it down quickly in the gloom of my poky kitchen. I then mixed another glassful and sipped it more slowly this time, flipping up the blind to reveal the gravestone skyline of East London. Through the rain-spattered window of my fifth-floor flat, I could just make out the NatWest tower to the right, a monumental City marker barely visible in the gloom. Closer to home, on the left, near a rusting, rubble-strewn skeleton of a half-abandoned industrial estate, two heavily scaffolded gas cooling towers were in the process of being dismantled, brick by brick, row by row, like unravelling knitting. I could just make out the shiny blue logo of the Docklands light railway, which had opened not long ago to transport alien commuters to the broken heart of the East End, which was now undergoing major surgery for the benefit of property developers. Lights were beginning to be switched on in the drab council flats of the twin tower blocks just in front, and traffic was building up on the motorway that dipped in and out the Blackwall tunnel.

It was a grey, depressing, dirty day in the city I thought, as my head cleared, but it was getting late. Putting the empty glass on the worktop, I turned and went back to the telephone to call Max Winter at *Technology Week*.

When I finally got through, we had what is euphemistically described as "words". They were short, bitter, monosyllabic and Anglo-Saxon. The conclusion of our rather one-sided conversation was that tomorrow was press day, and dead cousins didn't need key *Technology Week* reporters to pay their respects until the day after. I pointed out that if he thought cousins weren't close enough kin to warrant special dispensation, he ought to

know that Julian had been like a brother to me. But I was
wasting my time. Max was brutally single-minded about
press day, and I would have needed to be attending my
own funeral to get out of it. I offered him Barnaby's tip
by way of a palliative, but it was about as effective as
offering a banana to a rampaging carnivore. Anyway, he
was right: as he said himself, he wanted a front-page story
not a down-page inside filler.

Defeated, I put the phone down with a defiant slam, my
heart pumping hard with anger. The man was an insensitive martinet who didn't deserve an ounce of effort from
me or anyone else who had the misfortune to work for him.
One bloody day, I thought – he could have let go just for
one bloody day. I paced up and down, biting the corner
of my right thumb. Then the phone rang. I snatched it up
and answered it brusquely. It was Anne.

"I thought, I'd ring you, again, George. I can't stand
those answering machines, and I wasn't sure you'd play
back your messages straight away." She sounded much
better now than she had done earlier – more her usual
self: sensible, calm, and controlled. I hadn't expected to,
but before I could speak, I started to cry. The tears were
two parts anger, one part grief, and more than a splash of
alcohol.

When I had recovered a little I told her that, as much
as I wanted to, I couldn't make it to the funeral; that my
job would be on the line if I missed press day; that my
editor was an unsympathetic brute who had it in for me. I
didn't tell her about the extended lunch which I knew had
stoked Max's temper. The worm of guilt had already begun
to wriggle deep inside me. The excuse that I had given
about press day sounded feeble but how could I explain the
galvanising presence of Max to her? Still, she was typically
gentle and understanding, sweetly reasonable about Max
and about my grubby job. They had both won a moral
victory, and I had lost, again.

Our conversation turned to reminiscences, but not for
long. We both realised that our thoughts were tacking
inexorably towards one point, one inescapable reef of

family scandal barely hidden under the surface of good manners and fine sensibilities. Of course, I was outmanoeuvred and reached it first.

"Anne, one thing I did want to ask. . .about Julian. . . how long did he have, um, this problem?" I said finally, as a taunting vision of him masked and plumply naked, but for wicked little strips of silk, appeared before me.

She replied with a sigh and a depressed, rather frustrated voice.

"Well, George, I didn't know about it – none of us did. How could we? It is not something he would have discussed, now, is it? I mean, how do you tell if someone is. . .well, that way inclined. . .even if he is your own brother? We have hardly seen him this year, and just talking to him over the phone, seeing him the occasional weekend and getting the odd postcard is not going to reveal much that you wouldn't put down to just being apart."

She stopped to gather her thoughts, and after a small silence, she continued, as if talking to herself. "I don't think he ever really grew up or settled. He wasn't very mature as an adult, although he seemed to be very mature as a child. Do you see what I mean?"

I didn't reply, probably because I would have to admit that I never felt very adult myself. At twenty-five I hadn't laid to rest the spotty ghost of my adolescence, so who was I to judge the immature remains of my poor dead cousin?

Anne continued to speak. "He had friends. He still saw a lot of Eddie. . .so he wasn't desperately lonely or anything. He was in the caving and potholing club. But no girlfriend, no one he spoke about anyway."

The idea that Julian, a plump, freckled closet tranvestite with a penchant for claustrophobic adventures, would have a sweet girl to introduce to the family was now too ludicrous to contemplate. I would have laughed had it not been for the mention of Eddie, whose very name made my skin prickle with animosity.

Eddie was my husband, a man whom I now regarded as a psychopath with a superb talent for impersonating a good guy. Ironically, we had met through Julian, who had befriended him while on summer camp in the United States. Ours was an unfortunate match that lasted just six months after we rushed to the registry office in a frothy romantic haze – or, to be more frank, in a state of high sexual tension. My parents were appalled, although they found Eddie very charming. That was the trouble, everybody found him charming. I did, too, until I found out he had been scoring with my good friend, Celia Stevenson.

"What about the inquest? What happened there?" I asked, coming back to the present.

"It was recorded as death through experimentation. . . Oh George, it was awful. . . and so embarrassing, you can't imagine. There was a witness, a local man."

"You mean someone was there while he. . .?" I was wide-eyed with anticipation.

"No, no, more's the pity. Julian might be alive today if someone had been there. No, this man was there on a previous occasion."

I was torn between wanting to reject fresh scandal and a perverse desire to be utterly amazed at the unsuspected depravity of someone who had always been so comfortably and boringly familiar.

"Go on," I whispered.

"An old fellow was passing Julian's cottage a month before. The door was open and the man's dog ran in. The man called out but the dog had gone upstairs, so he went in to find him and found Julian, you know, dressed up, hanging and everything. He said Julian was struggling for breath. The keys to his handcuffs had dropped onto the floor. The old man had to hand Julian the keys so he could unlock the cuffs, free his hands, and drag off his mask. The old fellow was quite sweet about it actually . . ."

"Did he drop them again this time?" I asked before she digressed.

"Well, no. . ." she paused, as if something had suddenly occurred to her. "No, he forgot them. They said he must have forgotten them. The police later found the keys in his desk drawer."

"Forgot his keys?"

It was a rhetorical question, for unless Julian had altered beyond all recognition, it was impossible to believe he could forget *anything*, still less something that was obviously crucial to the smooth running of such an important event.

"It is hard to believe, isn't it?" Anne volunteered after a long meditative silence.

"Anne, it is frigging, excuse me, impossible to believe," I said.

She didn't reply to that, and I didn't want to talk any more, so I apologised again about the funeral and told her I would see her later in the week – perhaps at the weekend. I offered to help her in the doleful task of cleaning Julian's things from his cottage. "I'll ring to tell you when I'll be down," I promised.

"All right, George," she said in her gentle, sweet, serious voice. "It will be so good to see you again."

I replaced the receiver and reset the answering machine. It was dark now, and cold in the flat, even with the block's communal central heating clanking into action. I clicked on the gas fire and felt my stomach beginning to rumble. I was starving. There wasn't much in the fridge either – grapefruit juice and soda water, a regulation bottle of cheap dry white wine, a wedge of Edam, a tub of ageing yoghurt, a pack of butter, a solitary suspect tomato and some sprouting cloves of garlic. The larger cupboard was just as deserted – a few tins of beans and cans of sardines, three strands of spaghetti, a packet of Swiss-style muesli, a bottle of HP sauce, coffee, tea and a buttery jar of marmalade. There was enough bread on the sideboard for me to cut a couple of slices and still leave some for breakfast. So, my supper was grilled cheese on toast with HP sauce, which I ate as the coffee warmed up. I leant against the sink unit to gaze out through the smutty raindrops at the lights of the city, and I recalled Julian as a boy: organised, orderly, methodical, with an almost military approach to our childish campaigns on the sunny beaches and in the grassy wooded hills. It was he who would draw up the timetables and the lists that ensured we were adequately prepared for the rigours of the school summer holidays. I still had a photograph of him somewhere, freckled and blond in baggy white shorts, as he made us lay out the contents of our back-packs and ticked everything off in a notebook. His socks were smooth and straight, held up under his perfectly proportioned knees by garters, the tags of which lay flat and equidistant. He always carried two clean handkerchiefs, one for himself and a spare for me, for the inevitable graze on my knee or elbow. He kept a shiny multi-bladed red and silver Swiss Army penknife in his pocket, with a piece of string and chocolate for emergencies. Julian had been our natural leader, guiding his cousins crocodile-fashion through the popping gorse, across the cliffs and down to the sea in our happy, salty, sunny holidays.

Poor Julian. The irony of it. There was I, having wanted desperately to a tumbling tousled boy; and there was he, wanting to be a girl in nice knickers. I shook my head. He never *forgot* a damned thing. He labelled, he listed, he classified. He was the only person I knew who archived his archive disks twice, in case of a computing disaster. A belt and braces man, by nature. And he would have been just as carefully precise in his secret passion, I was sure.

Julian's forgotten keys seemed almost as degenerate as his fatal flirtation with silk and rubber. It was totally out of character, but then what did I really know about that?

And what of his newly discovered talent? What had he done to get headhunted for such a juicy job in California?

I pulled the blind down and poured myself some more coffee before going into the living-room to check the mail in my personal computer. I dialled through my electronic mail-box and the bulletin board that I used. In my mail-box there was the same curt message from Max that he'd left on my answering machine, and a junk press release heralding the launch of a "unique" data communications device. On the bulletin board was a picture of Betty Boop

11

and a little epigram which said "The sex life of an electrician, part 2: fully excited Millie Amp mumbled 'OHM! OHM! OHM!'" It was not original and I guessed it was from that happy soul in the machine, Warren Graham, my friendly black hacker and the white knight in my life.

CHAPTER THREE

WARREN HAD BEEN A BRITISH Telecom engineer until he became a cab driver. He had warm, coffee-coloured, lightly pockmarked skin, hazel eyes, scruffy corkscrew hair, a big wide smile, perfect teeth – and, as it happens, he was a wizard with computers. He learned "the knowledge" in his unbelievably long lunch hours at BT, and I'd lived in the block a year before discovering that he resided upstairs. Fortunately he had noticed me, and was able to recognise and rescue me from Mile End station late one night while he was driving home and I was the worse for drink. It was at that dangerous time past midnight when women, sober or drunk, travelling on their own are considered negligent to their own welfare.

There was an ugly fight in process outside the underground station, and blood was spilling onto the street. Two men were being pulped in a most unpleasant manner by a group of smart, crop-haired, Italian-suited thugs, while five yards away I, oblivious in my inebriation, leaned out into the road with my arm up hailing taxis, who sensibly passed me by.

Warren told me all this the next morning when he roused me. It was well past eleven and he proceeded to hector me about my lifestyle. I was far too weak to tell him to mind his own business, and in any case, being nagged by him seemed to be the most natural thing in the world. The conversation was easy while he made us some tea, until I realised I was wearing nothing but a large Dallas Cowboys T-shirt. It wasn't that I was coy about exposing myself in unprepossessing night attire to strangers who happened by my kitchen, but I just couldn't remember getting undressed the night before. I couldn't remember anything except that I didn't own a Dallas

Cowboys T–shirt. Warren never explained, and I hadn't the courage to ask

I deleted my mail after leaving a fond, lowbrow "Hello, chickenshit" message on the bulletin board for him. I wasn't really in the mood for fooling around with dubious quotations.

Then it suddenly occurred to me that I hadn't got any details of the Californian software house that had headhunted Julian for its "lifestyle" programs. Any new software company is interesting and worth checking out, but this one had added curiosity value because it had headhunted my cousin for a fat fee. I had to find out what had attracted a West Coast entrepreneur to our shores, so I left a message for Barnaby, which I reckoned he would pick up either at the office or at home, providing he had actually made it back to either destination and sobered up. He could reply sometime that evening so I could make some calls later on when it would be afternoon in the States. I sent my message discreetly to Barnaby's private mailbox; it wouldn't do for his firm to find out. Warren would, of course, but he didn't count.

When I'd finished, I settled down on the sofa to watch the six o'clock news. There had been an aeroplane crash in Korea, a flare-up in the Lebanon, some national asset was up for privatisation, people were dying in Ethiopia, a hundred-year-old woman's advanced years had earned her a trip on Concorde; and City-watchers were focusing on a new post-Big Bang prodigy, Ms Kay Fisher, a young broker/dealer with the Midas Touch. I would have good reason to pay more attention to the petite, auburn-haired woman in the neat blue suit and cream bow-tie blouse, but I didn't know that then. Instead, as her cool image nodded and smiled, my eyelids slowly closed and I slept until midnight.

Heavy footsteps and loud voices of my low-rent neighbours staggering from the lift awakened me. I switched off the television and stumbled over to the PC to check for any messages. My head was aching and my mouth was dry. There was nothing from Barnaby, but something from

Warren: a smug but not unhelpful message containing the full address and telephone number of a firm called Lifestyle Software Inc., which I concluded – as Warren had – must have been Barnaby's client. Warren had added the footnote: "It doesn't exist. I tried it".

My friend had obviously been very bored that evening, and had decided that a prowl through the confidential databases of Hitec Executive Search Ltd might prove diverting. This story should run and run, I thought, and went to bed. Tomorrow was press day and I had to be in for 9.00am.

Press day started badly. My personal organiser, which I had discarded somewhere in the bedroom, had awoken me with a persistent, even-toned bleep a full hour after my digital radio should have done. I found it and switched it off, but it bleeped again, and a blithe three-word message tripped gaily around in a continuous loop through its thin-window, liquid-crystal display. It said "Happy Birthday, Eddie". We had been separated for two years, but that bossy, insensitive calculator could be programmed more than that length of time in advance. I opened my rather full laundry basket, dropped it in, and pulled on the clothes I had worn yesterday.

It was still raining, and I was running very late as I squeezed onto the steamy Central Line and travelled, pressed between the ample breasts of what appeared to be a large, but fashionable, intellectual worker peasant and the sweatshirted pectorals of a weightlifting type whose cheeks were raw with crusty acne. The carriage was jammed to over-capacity. Close by, there was a slight reek of curry and garlic mingled with spicy aftershave, but the over-whelming smell was one of damp fur and straw as the odour of rain-sodden white-collar workers permeated the air. We squeezed out as the doors slid open at Tottenham Court Road and I hurriedly pushed through the crowds and up to the filthy street. It was 9.30am, a busker was singing "Norwegian Wood" in the subway, and a dosser was asleep by his empty beer cans on the slimy stairs.

When I reached Old Compton Street and the offices of

Technology Week, the tobacco smoke was already so thick that you could almost feel the nicotine and tar precipitating out from the noxious smog. The team was already working hard and Max was esconced in his wheelchair, centre stage of his theatre of news and sales. Sitting at his computer terminal, he seemed as if physically plugged in to the network. Although he had an apartment above the offices, it was as if he never left them. No one had ever arrived early enough or left late enough to see that space empty. He was an electronic newshound, and that meant scavenging through the narrow world of international information networks like a modern-day Prince of Darkness. He didn't look up when I arrived, and I was very glad. It was far too early for a confrontation with Max.

My desk was by a window with a totally obscured view of the busy Soho street. The sill was stacked high with old newspapers and computer magazines, and the stub of an African Violet that I had struggled to keep alive. That day there were three-day-old messages struck to the side of my terminal: one from Anne, one from my solicitor, and one from Eddie. I gritted my teeth and pushed aside a large pile of fresh mail, the *Wall Street Journal* and the *Financial Times*, which lay across old piles of paper and spiral notebooks. A two-day tower of press releases was beginning a long slide into a wastepaper bin which had been strategically placed behind my desk. I pressed a button on my terminal and logged on.

The on-going news roster had me working on three stories: a multi-million-pound order for computers for a broker, a possible joint venture to provide an electronic funds transfer system for the banks, and a yarn about incompatible computer systems fouling up a building society merger. My name was also down for a discursive feature on computer systems in the City post-Big Bang. Max wanted me to analyse the success and/or failures of electronic systems introduced as a result of new stock-market trading methods and rules imposed on the financial centre of the UK in 1986. Fortunately, it wasn't for today's deadline, but I would have to start setting up some interviews soon.

By 3.30pm I had filed all the stories, just. My back ached, my clothes reeked of tobacco smoke, but I was relieved and satisfied to have done my job. I leaned back in my chair, with my booted feet in the top drawer of my desk, and bit into a Big Mac. Warm mayonnaise and shreds of lettuce trickled down my chin and, as I reached over for a French fry, I spotted a note in the carton. It was from Charlie East, the deputy City editor who'd been out for orders for lunch. He'd written: "Holding Amstrad, sold Atlantic, bought Systems, divvy up £750, drinks tonight at the Crown." I smiled and took a large satisfying chunk of hamburger. It was great news. Some of the sales reps and the reporters ran a covert investment club, with Charlie as the fund manager. Six of us had invested about £200 each, and apart from some near disasters early on, Charlie was riding high on the bull market. He had dealt only with electronics firms to date – a bit risky considering that he was in a position to make more than an educated guess sometimes. Lately he'd been talking about traded options, but I wasn't sure he could handle the complications of that market. I was thinking of taking my cut and calling it a day, especially since I thought we were living on borrowed time as far as Max finding out was concerned.

With the deadlines over, the noise of the office machinery began to dominate. The reps were still trying to close, printers were printing, faxes were faxing, copiers were copying, but the keyboards were growing silent; all the stories had been filed to the network, the subs and Max. Across the room a group of journalists stood chatting and sorting through what remained in a large box of food orders. No one had made lunch at the normal time that day.

The open-plan, overcrowded, offices are a testament to Max's faith in economics not ergonomics. Good journalists, he said, don't need comfortable chairs, because he didn't expect them to sit in them long enough to notice. Good display, classified and subscription reps only required a constant supply of ashtrays, wall space for pin-ups, and the opportunity for good commission to keep them happy.

Few people were in a hurry to leave *Technology Week* in spite of the joke that the industry's "going" rate was the inevitable salary increase achieved by anyone who left our paper to join another. This unmaterialistic attitude to employee motivation had created the most profitable and widely-read paper in the computer industry. The fact that 150,000 or so readers were prepared to pay for it when they received, for free, ten similar publications on their desk at the same time, was proof of Max's maxim that if something is worth reading, it's worth buying.

I wiped my face and hands and leaned forward to pick the old messages from my terminal. The one from Anne reminded me of Julian's funeral, for the first time that day, and I realised grimly that I had no idea whether he was to be buried or cremated. The idea of his body in a trundling coffin being winched behind a mauve curtain towards the eternal flame filled me with disgust.

"A decent burial – he should have a decent burial, at least," I muttered.

I assumed Barnaby and his Californian employers were already searching hard for his replacement. Whoever it would be, he or she was to be envied. I figured that to gain Hitec £50,000 in commission, Julian would have been earning at least $150,000 – plus the emoluments Barnaby had described. That represented very "serious" money indeed for an analyst/programmer working for a fast food franchise for £12–15,000 per annum – as Julian had been. He had worked for a motorway pull-in pizza house with outlets all over the country. Good business, perhaps, but it was hard to imagine such an organisation being seen as at the leading edge of software development. Perhaps Julian had been working on a special project; after all he must have had *something* to attract a Californian software outfit so bright and new that it had not even installed a telephone. Such a firm would surely be unlikely to come to England in search of a common-or-garden computer programmer when there was such embarrassment of riches in that field at home.

Barnaby had dismissed poor Julian as talentless, but I

put that down to bitterness at losing his fee. Julian must have been a specialist of some kind, and if he was, I figured his old firm would know. There was a tickle of a story here, even without the added ingredient of Julian's strange demise, and that was a *personal* mystery which I thought was best left alone. If I could find out what Julian actually did, I would be able to discover an important factor in the make-up of a West Coast firm which was fresh on the market with some intriguing new software ideas. It would be a good story for *Technology Week*, and could even turn out to be more than just a filler.

It was almost 4.00pm, and I decided that if I hung around I could check Lifestyle's number myself. In the meantime, I decided to ring Julian's firm. The number was in my contact book, and I jabbed at the digits on my telephone with fresh energy. After a few seconds a chirpy voice replied: "Pull Up for Pizza Ltd."

I asked for the personnel department, and was immediately put on hold in the company of a dotty digital rendering of 'Santa Lucia.'

"Personnel," said a voice not a moment too soon.

I introduced myself. "I'm Georgina Powers from the computer industry paper, *Technology Week*. I am trying to trace Julian Kirren, one of your programmers."

I was put on hold again with 'Santa Lucia', and after a minute the voice said, "I'm putting you through."

"Good afternoon. I'm Mrs Forbes. How can I help you?" said the smooth-talking Mrs Forbes.

I identified myself again, well aware that by now she'd had plenty of time to think.

"Mr Kirren did work here, but he gave in his notice two weeks ago. I don't know if you know this but, sadly, he has since passed away."

"Oh yes, that's why I'm calling," I said, quickly deciding on an excuse for calling. "We want to publish an obituary on him. We understand he was especially talented in his field."

There was a non-committal silence before her answer.

"I will have to put you through to the data-processing

department, if you need specialist information. However, I can say that he was an extremely conscientious and methodical employee," she said, not wishing to lose an opportunity to appear in print. "Wait one moment."

More strains of "Santa Lucia" until the data-processing manager, one Arthur Piggott, tuned in. He explained that Julian had been engaged in migrating software from one machine to another. The company had installed a new mini-computer system, and the department was currently heavily involved in protecting its software investment by adapting the computer programs which had run on the old machine to run on the new. It was arduous, methodical work, but hardly "hold the front page" news. Mr Piggott claimed he had no knowledge of Julian's new venture, adding that he had tendered his notice at a most inconvenient time.

When I probed a little on Julian's death, he was admirably reticent. "An odd business," he said briskly, moving rapidly on to a subject on which he felt strongly: the executive search firm which had poached Julian from his team. Headhunting, he added was an obnoxious profession; he was tired of training people and losing them to those who couldn't be bothered to do so themselves – upstart American firms were the thin edge of the wedge which would prise open the door to let foreign hordes steal our national resources. If I wanted to write a story, he said I should consider something on that topic. I thanked him for his time, and terminated the interview.

Julian's work, as described by Mr Piggott, had been routine programming. Either he was not revealing the complete picture, which was professionally understandable, or Julian had been working on something independently. Lifestyle's software was obviously aimed at the mass market, and I knew that most success stories in mass-market software started with one idea around which a company was built. At least one of the company's founders would have written the program, then the company would buy in management and financial help, if it needed it. It was unusual for a small new firm to go headhunting for programming talent. I had to assume that, despite Barnaby's sour remarks, Julian must have had that talent, some particularly sought-after skill. One thing was certain, Barnaby would be hard at work trying to retrieve that commission.

I reached out my hand to dial his number, but the phone rang before I could begin. It was Max.

"Could I see you for a moment, please, Georgina?"

Oh shit, I thought.

"Certainly," I said, as coolly as possible, and rose slowly to pick my way across the electrical cables and discarded paper debris of the day. Finally I stood by his desk and looked down at him. He was editing something on screen and did not look up, so I waited, arms folded. Max was not an unattractive man, but he had what the tolerant would describe as an unfortunate manner. He communicated with his colleagues via telephone or terminal, or in brusque monologues at weekly briefing sessions. When he was angry, he shouted; and when he was pleased, he said nothing. No one on the team really knew much about him outside work. Legend had it that he had ripped his legs to pieces and destroyed his back coming out of a bend at the Le Mans 24-Heures motorcycle race; and that when once asked if he had any regrets about it, he had said, "The Ducatti."

But he had a two good things going for him: firstly he was the undisputed *numero uno* of the international computer publishing scene, and, secondly, what rankled with our major competitors was that he could not be bought because he owned fifty per cent of the *Technology Week* stable. His partner, Ray Williams, operated from a small office on the same floor, and took care of everything but the editorial. Max demanded high quality, and that is what he got, despite being as tight as a nut with salaries and spare with the "by-lines". A story had to be either exclusive or very, very, good to have the writer's name underneath. "Money is no motivator," he would say often enough, "but reputation is" – a remark it's easy to pass when you own fifty per cent of a company.

As I waited, I noted that his thick, reddish hair was thinning at the front, and his very short beard glinted gold on his pale, blue-veined skin. He gave a few final taps on his keyboard, to save the text he had been working on, then he looked up.

"Do sit down, Georgina," he said, gesturing with a calloused hand to the seat by his desk and moving an ashtray to the other side. I was intrigued by this unusually considerate behaviour. Max rarely had anything to impart that would warrant such courtesy, and what followed was quite out of character.

"I would like to thank you for coming in today," he continued, looking back at his screen and concentrating hard on its blankness. Then he caught me by surprise by looking back at me quickly with his unnerving eyes: one brown and one flecked with jade green. I stared at him for an instant until I registered that he had finished and was expecting some sort of reply. My face warmed as my cheeks reddened infuriatingly.

"I wasn't given much choice, was I?" My answer seem to spit angrily from my lips as involuntarily as the blush had crept up my neck.

There was a tense silence. Max placed his broad hands together and pushed his rough fingers together as if in prayer.

"It's the nature of the job, Georgina," he said at last in a dry, resigned manner. It was a cliché and he knew it, but I was struggling to hold back the hot, inexplicable tears that teetered frustratingly at corners of my eyes. There was another long, tense silence while Max sat there controlled and unemotional, and I struggled to hold back the bitter words I wanted to shout at him.

"Let's forget about it, shall we?" I said curtly at last, and rose to go. I had wanted to take tomorrow off to help Anne at Julian's cottage, but there was no way my pride would allow me to ask permission now.

"Just a minute, George. . .ina," Max spoke, clearly exasperated. "It is maybe too late now, but if you need to take time off this week, please do so. I realise you must have, er. . matters to attend to now."

Someone with greater sensibility would have gained

more from the situation than Max had. He had tried to be magnanimous, apologetic and generous, all in one go, but his coldness had turned his efforts into condescension. The fact that there was now only Friday left in the working week possibly had not occurred to him. I pitied him his social ineptitude, but the feeling soon evaporated when Max added:

"Don't forget to follow up that tip about the Californian software house, though. It could be interesting."

I nodded my head in an exaggerated and facetious manner, but he had already turned back to his terminal, the screen of which was again alive with numbers and characters as he logged on to some information database somewhere else in the world. That man never misses a trick, I thought, relieved that he had returned to his old self. If there was one thing worse than Max acting in character, it was Max straining the milk of human kindness.

It was dark now, and the office was almost empty. Being after six, there was no point in calling Warren on the telephone; he'd be taking advantage of the cheap period to make his computer calls. I tapped in a message, via my terminal, for his bulletin board, inviting him to come with me tomorrow to Julian's cottage outside Milton Keynes. Then I closed down my system, ready for work on Monday, and made one international call to Lifestyle Software. Warren was *almost* right: the number did exist but it had been disconnected. As I left the office for a quick drink at the Crown, I caught sight of Max smiling to himself.

CHAPTER FOUR

WARREN WAS IN A GRISLY mood and hardly spoke during the bone-rattling journey up the M11. He'd awoken me rather churlishly with angry digs at my door buzzer at gone 10 am, and I was feeling rather fragile from the night before.

"Your skin looks disgusting," he said, making me some tea.

"Thanks," I yawned, as I made my way to the bathroom.

"Good night? You were back late," he remarked when I had dressed and returned.

"Not bad. A few of us went down The Crown. Charlie was on form, so I stayed a little longer than I had planned. . .What about you? How'd you get on last night?" I said, pushing my hair back with one hand and gulping down the hot dark tea.

Warren ignored my question. He was looking in the kitchen cupboards.

"There ain't much here. What do you want – toast?" he said sniffily.

"Yes, thanks, toast. I think I've got some bread left."

"Two slices."

"One for you, one for me," I said, hiding my rising irritation as best I could.

"I've eaten."

"In that case, two for me. . . please."

Warren wasn't usually such a pain in the ass. I wanted to slap his hand away from the grill and tell him to get lost, but I thought better of it. I needed him, after all. It did occur to me that he might have thought it a cheek to be summoned for some assignation in the country by a vague last-minute telephone call, but he'd

24

never complained when I'd asked him to help me out in the past.

"What's up?" I said, instead, to his stubborn back.

"Nuffink."

"There is."

"Forget it."

He delivered the toast to the table and waved me to sit down. I did so with a display of little real appetite.

"Eat it," he said.

I fiddled with a bit of toast while Warren sat opposite me. Eventually, I put it down and spoke.

"Look, Warren, I know it's short notice and everything, but this could be important. I need you to help me."

"Need me?" he said sourly. "Now what would a hot-shot, piss-artist journo like you need me for?"

I was shocked by his uncharacteristic aggressiveness and bit back a sharp answer. Instead, I patiently explained that the address he had fished out of Hitec's database had been the future employer of my recently deceased cousin. Without going into too much lurid detail, I described the manner of Julian's death and what I wanted to find out.

"I know he had his own personal computer so I want you to help me check it out, and perhaps have a go at breaking into my cousin's old firm to look through his computer files there. He must have been doing *something* to catch the eye of Lifestyle, and I want to know what it was."

Warren seemed to cheer up fractionally at the thought of a little electronic joyriding. He got up and left me finishing my meagre breakfast while he collected a few items from his flat. Ten minutes later we were on the road.

Anne was at the door when we arrived at Julian's russet-coloured cottage in Thatchford, a small, charming dormitory village with easy access to the brave new metropolis of Milton Keynes and the doughty old market trader, London itself. As I opened the little wrought-iron gate, she looked a little surprised that the cabbie didn't drive off immediately.

"Where's your friend?" she called out, her voice sounding rather plummy after the sharp patois of inner London.

"He's just getting the cab off the road a bit," I replied, giving her a big hug. She seemed small and fragile.

"Ah. I see," she said, and I suspected the remark disguised a well-trodden thought process which concluded that cousin George should perhaps be forgiven, because she had always had a penchant for adopting scruffy strays and choosing "unconventional" friends. I forgave her assumption because she had been engaged to a solicitor from Welwyn for about three year, and, unlike me, had caused hardly a ripple in the still quiet pond that was our family life. My own impetuosity had disturbed the calm of filial relationships more than once, but now all that paled before Julian's personal disaster, which must have begun a churning in our family that perhaps would never subside.

I looked over at Warren, who was now crossing the little rustic lane. His hand were thrust into his faded jeans, and his brown leather jacket swung back away from his hips. Bathed in the chestnut, autumnal glow of this leaf-strewn English hamlet, he looked alien, like a tall bright sunflower framed in the red rose-buttoned arch of a wooden trellis. Despite our earlier estrangement, I felt a surge of protectiveness towards him. After all, it was I who had brought him here to this strange countryside, away from his natural *A to Z* habitat of double-backs, one-ways, flyovers, and sharp city streets. Anyway, Anne was wrong: it was Warren who adopted and cared for scruffy strays.

She showed us graciously into the front room, and when we were all seated in the paisley-patterned armchairs with our cups of tea on our laps, she made a formal announcement.

"I am not quite sure, but I think we have had a little break-in."

She placed her cup and saucer on the tray, turned her light-lashed blue eyes towards us and, brushing an odd strand of blond hair behind her small, neat ear, she continued.

"I haven't called the police because I'm not sure what, if anything, has been taken. No doors have been forced, or anything, so I presume whoever it was had a key. I've checked all the rooms in the house, and things that might normally have been taken are still here. . ." she pointed at the video recorder and the stereo ". . .but the study is not as it should be."

"What do you mean?" I asked.

"Well, it is rather like those newspaper competitions when you have two pictures of the same scene and you have to pick out ten small changes in the second picture. I am not sure that anything has gone, but I am sure something has changed. Come and have a look."

We all climbed the narrow staircase to Julian's study, and it was very strange walking into the room where he had died. I looked up and was shocked to see a sturdy steel hook fixed in the ceiling – a stark, ludicrous memento of Julian's death. The tidy grey-carpeted room was gloomy even though the day outside was quite bright. In one corner were an old office desk, with a blank-faced beige-coloured personal computer on its smooth wooden surface, and a second-hand typist's chair tucked underneath.

There were shelves above the desk. The lowest was not flush with the wall, and it bore a printer with a sheaf of continuous stationery folding fan-like down the back; the others were lined with variegated boxes of different computer programs and manuals. There was a small steel two-drawer filing cabinet in another corner, and also a bookshelf. There was no clutter, no mess, just a little dust.

"So what's wrong?" I asked

"Well, when I was here the other day it didn't look so. . .so empty. I was the last to leave after the funeral, and I locked up," Anne replied.

"You might be feeling a bit depressed about the place," I said gently to her. "Still, you're right, if someone has been here, they must have had a key."

In the shadows of the study, Anne's face showed the strain of the past week. She looked rather lost as she peered about, frowning, and bit her lip when Warren put his bag down and started to check out Julian's program library, running his long brown fingers across the multi-coloured boxes.

I went to the toilet, and came back to find Warren seated in front of the computer. It was a hard-disk machine, which meant that Julian would have saved the programs and files which we would see in a directory on the screen as soon as the machine was switched on and booted up. Warren did this, and we could see that nothing but the operating system remained.

"He *must* have some back-up disks. Where are his disks?" Warren asked, looking around for Julian's archives.

"That's it!" said Anne moving quickly towards the desk with a sigh of relief. "I knew there was something missing. Three boxes of them were there, right by the machine." She pointed to a vacant space by the desk, which we could now see bore faint dust-lined oblong imprints where the boxes had once stood.

Warren checked through the desk drawers and the shelves, and I looked elsewhere around the room. No disks, therefore no records, I thought. Then Warren dipped into his bag and pulled out a box-of-tricks called Scorn: a neat little program which can check a disk for records and files that have been deleted. When a computer user deletes a file, the information on the disk isn't scrubbed clean. The file name is deleted from the directory, so to all intents and purposes it has been apparently wiped out. All that really happens is that the portion of disk it occupied is now flagged as available to be overwritten with fresh information. A program like Scorn can find and reveal old files as easily as Victorian sleuths used to find the secret notes of villains pressed into a blotter. To destroy the information, you need to physically destroy the disk.

But Warren found no villain's imprint. However, that wasn't wholly unsuspicious. Instead of fragments of partly deleted and overwritten files, the disk bore nothing but lines and lines of zeros. Someone had made sure that whatever was left on the disk had been written over so no one could piece together the jigsaw and read even one line of text that might reveal itself.

"Hmmm. . .whoever cleared up in here was keener to

eliminate what was on the disk than to disguise the fact that he, or she, had been here. Overwriting is a dead giveaway," he said.

"He," I replied sardonically. "The toilet seat was up."

"What about in here?" Anne said quickly, pointing to the filing cabinet. "If there aren't any electronic records, perhaps there are some paper records of interest."

I walked over to help her. There was nothing much, just some names and addresses of potholing and caving clubs, lists of club members, a couple of catalogues for dubious products, and and various household files for bills.

The folders were arranged alphabetically. As we flicked through them we realised one was missing – the one which would have been labelled K/L. The letter K meant nothing much to me, but the letter L did. It would have been the folder for anything concerning Lifestyle Software, Inc.

"Anne, did you check Julian's suitcases?" I asked.

"No, but they are still in his bedroom," she said, pointing the way.

The light canvas bags were neatly packed, ready for his flight, but we couldn't find the destination tags or the ticket. We searched the cottage thoroughly for any clue which would link Julian to Lifestyle, California, or even to Hitec, but it was futile. Whoever had been here had removed all trace of any link with Lifestyle Software and had done so very effectively, with the minimum of visible disruption.

The tickle of a story on Lifestyle Software, Inc. that I had felt yesterday was becoming an ache now that the mysterious company, or someone connected with it, was evidently trying to extricate itself from any connection with Julian, and presumably with Julian's death.

"Do you think we should call the police?" said Anne, as we gathered again in Julian's study.

"It is a bit iffy, I agree, but I don't think we have enough to tell 'em yet," said Warren, whom I suspected really wanted to forestall any involvement by the police while there was any chance of hacking to do. I tried to explain the situation to Anne.

"Look, we want to find out what Julian was working on, first. I tried to trace Lifestyle, and so did Warren, but its number is disconnected. We can find no record of any link with Lifestyle here, even though Julian was due to join them next week. His old company reckons Julian was working on bog standard programming, so we want to know why Lifestyle found him interesting in the first place. There might be a clue in Julian's computer system at work, but I don't think we'd get permission to go in and poke around on their system for something that Julian shouldn't have been doing in their time. If he was doing something legitimately for them, they obviously find it too commercially sensitive to let us in on it. We have to find out whether they are lying, or whether Julian was stealing time on their computer for his own private work."

"So, what are you planning on, George?" she replied wearily, trying to absorb the fresh incongruities surrounding her brother's life.

"Well, we're going to have a go at hacking their system – or, rather, Warren is."

"Hacking?" she enquired with the grave surprise of an Old Bailey judge who has just been introduced to evidence of an alternative lifestyle as removed from his established life as a parallel universe.

I explained to her that we were going to try to use Julian's computer to break into the computer at his old company.

"Is that legal?" she asked.

"Well, not exactly, but it's not illegal. Well, not exactly, it's sort of . . . well, discouraged."

"Very clear that, Georgie babe," said Warren, looking around the back of the computer and then down underneath the desk, and then pointing out that Julian's modem had also been removed; only the cable remained. He looked up at the shelves.

"Yeh, the comms software has gone, too," he said to himself.

He then looked across at us and smiled, revealing the clean edges of his perfect white teeth.

"Never mind, ay? I happen to have about my person a rather clever little modem and some communications software of my own. Any chance of some grub?" he said rubbing his hands together.

It was half past four and we hadn't eaten since breakfast, so we clattered down the stairs after Anne into the small, light kitchen of the cottage. Warren opened the back door and stepped out into the fading sunshine, which was retreating from the fairly large, plain but well-kept garden. He took a deep breath of the autumn air and walked over to some small apple trees which stood where the garden met an open field.

Anne put the kettle on and placed some chops she had brought under the grill. She was a head shorter than me, ash blond, and neatly dressed in a vibrant blue mohair jumper and skirt. I felt bulky and scruffy by comparison. Her hair was beautifully cut in a fashionable bob, but she was wearing less make-up than she usually did: just a hint of burgundy lipstick, shiny and wet, on her small round lips. I could smell some sort of exotic cinnamon perfume as she moved about.

"How did the funeral go, Anne?" I said, pulling up a chair and swinging my legs astride it so that I could lean my chin and arms on the back. Any offer of help would have just slowed things up.

She didn't look up from the chopping board, and carried on slicing the ripe red tomatoes, but from the side I could see her eyes moisten. After a moment, she composed herself and answered.

"Oh, it went quite well. The vicar said some nice things. Your parents came, George, and they asked after you. I explained how you'd wanted to come but your boss was not very understanding."

"And were they?" I inquired sarcastically.

Anne glanced at me with an admonishing look, and then turned to the sizzling chops.

"Eddie was there. He was quite upset," she said, placing

the lid on a saucepan of potatoes. "He asked after you – said he'd tried to get in touch."

I didn't answer.

"Seems to be doing very well. . .he's a dealer or something in the City . . .on a fantastic salary. Well, they all are there, aren't they?" She scraped the sliced tomatoes into the frying-pan and emptied some peas into another boiling pot.

"Was Julian buried, Anne? I'd like to visit the grave," I said, feeling increasingly morbid.

"No, he was . . . cremated. Mother wanted to take him home."

Tacky, I thought, but said no more. The silence in the small kitchen was broken only by the frying and popping of fat on the chops.

After a while I stretched up to look out the window, and could see Warren reaching for apples. Anne placed some cutlery on the table, and smoothed out the cloth with her creamy, burgundy-tipped hands. Her little sapphire and diamond engagement ring sparkled as she placed plates and buttered bread around the table.

"About the sleeping arrangements, George. . ." she said, nonchalantly pouring my tea. "There is only one room, so if you like, I can sleep on the settee."

Now there was a thought that hadn't occurred to me: Warren as my lover and not simply my friend. To me he was a companion, someone who bailed me out, nursed my hangovers, and nagged me about my personal habits. Whether eating or otherwise. What did I do for him? Nothing. . .except perhaps to pass him a few test programs that I acquired free through *Technology Week*. We went to a few parties together, clubs, pubs, and even late, late movies from time to time. I liked to watch him playing around with his computers and interfering with other people's. He never spoke of his family, but, though he was a solitary type, he had friends, or rather connections. But I couldn't even say whether he slept with men or women; he never talked about sex, and never mentioned love.

I'd told him about Eddie, my husband, though I had

never told anyone else what he'd meant to me or how badly he had hurt me. Warren was a good listener, quiet, gentle, sincere, if a little passionless. Eddie, on the other hand, was a liar and a shit, a shallow and unconscionable shyster, who had fooled me with his dark good looks, hot sweet kisses, and fly-blown promises. Worse, he had destroyed my faith in my own judgement. I had had to make hard rules for myself to live by, to protect myself from my own foolish weakness. Love was no longer on the agenda. If I couldn't distinguish the good from the bad, I didn't want it at all. Freedom of choice was more important, I thought: dalliances, uninvolved little liaisons unhindered by conscience – or hope. Warren was my friend, a good friend, and I didn't want to spoil such a precious relationship with love, or sex.

"I don't think so, Anne. Warren is just a friend, so I think he'll sleep on the settee; if he sleeps at all tonight, that is," I replied, just as Warren appeared at the door and looked down at us, his arms full of rosy apples.

It was dark when we finished our meal. Warren had praised Anne and made her laugh. He was a little ingratiating, I thought, but she obviously enjoyed his company. When we'd cleared up, Warren went upstairs to set up the computer, and I volunteered to help Anne with her inventory of Julian's belongings. Most of the stuff was marked down for charity or for auction; the family had already selected its souvenirs. I had my pick of the computer programs, some of which would be useful, but I really wanted his Swiss Army knife, and Anne said I could have it if we found it.

After about an hour and a half, we took some coffee up to Warren, who was tweaking the socket for the modem cable at the back of the computer.

Endemic self-interest within the computer industry means that standardisation is the exception rather than the rule. There is no such thing as "just plugging in" to a computer. While Warren tried to get his kit to fit Julian's, Anne and I started to hunt for Julian's password and the number of his old firm's computer.

Warren had come well prepared: he'd brought an auto-dialling modem; an electronic box which automatically dials numbers and translates computer messages into a form suitable for transmission over a telephone line. He had also remembered to bring a little utility program that he had written, which would search through a whole series of numbers and get the autodialler to dial them while it checked if the answer at the end of the line was man or machine generated. His communications software was sophisticated, and comprised a program which would make Julian's PC – his personal computer – mimic a range of popular machines which are used regularly in conjunction with larger minicomputers and mainframes.

Julian just might have left his company computer's telephone number somewhere in the study. He would certainly have stored it in his computer, but that was of no use to us now. As we searched, our suspicions that the mystery intruder must have removed any hard copy of that, too, were confirmed. But all was not lost: I had the company's main switchboard number, and our intruder hadn't removed the telephone directory. Together they would provide a range of numbers that Warren's little program could use to set off Julian's computer dialling hundreds of number permutations until we had a few possible winners. I had made the assumption that, being a franchise organisation with a number of outlets all over the country, Julian's firm would have set up its computer to communicate over telephone lines and exchange information with those outlets. If it wasn't connected to the telephone network, we were dead.

Getting the number with the help of the program and the autodialler would take time, but if it didn't work Warren might just have to give in and ask one of his mates at British Telecom for a favour – though he'd be reluctant to do that. He liked to save up his credits with them for really big kills.

Once we had the number, dialled it, and heard the welcoming whistle from the target computer's modem, our troubles would really begin. Computers only co-operate with compatible terminals or computers, so, with the help of his communications software, Warren would have to work out how to make Julian's PC acceptable to the pizza house's computer. He would have to get its face to fit. The PC would have to emulate an acceptable terminal, and that was never easy. The very flexibility of the program assumes a certain expertise in the user. Though not designed for those mischievous experts who call themselves hackers, it is, of course, extremely useful to them. Most hackers don't know all the details of the computer they are trying to break into, and this software allows them to form the right credentials as they are actually breaking in.

Once we had broken in, we would have to log on to the system and produce a password. I assumed that the pizza house wouldn't be too security conscious. Some companies are really tough about allocating passwords; others don't even issue them. If Julian had one and we hadn't found it written down anywhere in the study, we would have to second-guess him, or some other employee, just to get into the system.

"Right, what have we got by way of numbers?" said Warren, slapping his hands together and flexing his fingers like a pub pianist preparing to hammer the ivories.

"We haven't found a number or a password. But here's the pizza house number and a range from the local directory," I said, handing him a slip of paper that Anne and I had been filling in as we lay on the floor poring over the telephone book.

"A pizza house?" Warren looked up unenthusiastically. "Your cousin worked for a pizza house?"

"Pull Up For Pizza – you know, those ones at the motorway services."

"Christ, Georgina." His shoulders slumped and he looked sulkily away from me.

"What's wrong with that? Oh, come on, Warren, I know it's not very exciting, but a hack is a hack and this is important."

35

No one spoke. Anne and I stood by Warren like wide-eyed waifs awaiting reprieve by a schoolmaster's desk. It seemed an age before he grudgingly muttered "OK" and set his little dialling program to work.

Some hours and several cups of coffee later, we heard the whistle of the pizza house computer.

"Piece of piss," Warren said, his eyes fixed hard on the screen and his smokey-brown fingers twitching across the keyboard as he tried to match Julian's PC to the pizza house computer. Information kept appearing and disappearing, until a steady message stopped dead on the black screen. In glowing green letters it stated:

WELCOME. YOU ARE NOW CONNECTED TO PULL UP FOR PIZZA'S DRAC MINICOMPUTER SYSTEM RUNNING DRAC/VS VERSION 5.1.

After a few moments the message changed to a simple question:

USER NAME?

Warren typed in J.Kirren. It responded with the same request, so Warren tried J/Kirren.

It was the correct format, and another command appeared:

PASSWORD?

"Any suggestions?" said Warren, arbitrarily typing 123456789 while asterisks appeared on screen. That was a software precaution to prevent snooping eyes spying over people's shoulders at passwords as they were tapped in and appeared on screen.

PASSWORD?

Warren typed in FRED, but the computer was adamant. The screen was blank but for its simple password request. We tried all the most popular passwords commonly used by the less security-conscious, including DEMO, TEST, SYSTEM MANAGER, SYSOP, CHECK, REMOTE and HELP. The green unblinking message stoically remained.

PASSWORD?

"Try 'password'," I said.

Warren did so but there was still no movement.

"What's the business again? Pizzas?" he asked, and then

36

typed in PIZZA. Still no go. Then we tried a whole menu, including MOZZARELLA and DEEP PAN, without much success.

PASSWORD?

We began to get frustrated.

"Where's the nearest outlet? We could ring them up and get someone else's password," I suggested.

"Surely people don't just hand out this sort of information so easily?" Anne said in disbelief.

"You'd be surprised what someone posing as a DRAC service engineer can get," I replied. "It's a pretty common system, and the company's service side is huge. We've used that wheeze before and it's worked."

"Oh, really!" she said indignantly.

We tried ten more minutes of futile word-play, until Warren finally said "Bollocks" and tapped hard on the keyboard.

The screen command politely disappeared, and a passage of information detailing that we were in a sector of the disk allocated to J/Kirren appeared. Warren could hardly contain himself as he typed "DIRECTORY" and a list of programs and files that Julian had been working on filled the screen. Warren swore – with pleasure, I presumed – and Anne and I whooped in triumph.

"Warren, you are brilliant, brilliant, me old mate. Why didn't I think of that! But I'd have thought my cousin would have been a bit more sophisticated than that!" I laughed and hugged him as he scanned Julian's directory.

"That wasn't it." Warren replied, his fingers tapping relentlessly.

"Oh. What was it then?"

"Rubber."

"Oh shit," said Anne glumly.

The main directory of Julian files, programs and programming tools indicated that there were some other subdirectories. There was one in which he kept memos he had written, and one which listed in date order what he had been working on and when. We scanned the screen for clues, but I could feel that Warren wasn't particularly interested in this system.

"It's pretty straightforward programming work," he sighed, pushing his spine into the back of the chair as he stretched his legs.

"Let's see what he was working on the day that he died," I suggested, and Warren brought up the directory which held the files in time and date order.

The last entry caught me unawares. My stomach felt as if it had just experienced the sharp and shocking dip of a rollercoaster ride. I gripped Warren's shoulder to stay his hand. It was nearly 11.30 pm on a Friday night, and all Julian's programs should have been as dead as he was. Yet according to the entry there was a program running at that very moment. The computer had recorded it in its memory like an empty beach of sand bearing the clear fresh outline of a footstep.

"You did just log on, didn't you, Warren?" I said.

"Yeh, but this program could be set to run as soon as someone logs on. It could be a security trap."

Somehow I was unconvinced.

"It's running all right, but what is it doing? There's nothing on screen to indicate any background work. Let's find out what it is before we go any further," I said. "It's listed as 'MESS.EXE'. Let's go back to the directory and see if we can find any other files with the same prefix."

It was another half an hour before Warren said anything more. Anne meanwhile had decided to go to bed.

"Wake me if anything happens," she had said wearily.

I went and made some more coffee, and sat with Warren as he worked through the programs. We pulled out everything that could have been remotely related to "MESS-EXE". Warren knew what I wanted. When a programmer writes a program the result is lines and lines of computer code – a so-called program listing – usually written in a high-level language which a human being can understand but that the computer's microprocessor cannot. In the good old days, programmers had to enter program instructions one step at a time by physically setting a bank of switches up or down to form a code the machines understood. Today, programmers might use keyboards, and write programs using English-like "high-level" programming languages, but computers still "think" in "low-level" machine code. Therefore a computer's microprocessor has to translate the coded instructions written in the programmer's language into its own machine code before it can execute or run, the program.

So, once they have written it, programmers often "compile" the source program into machine code. That way it takes up less space on disk and in memory, and will also run faster because it is already in machine code, and so the processor doesn't get bogged down in translating it. The other benefit is that if someone tries to see the program, the screen fills with the incomprehensible gobbedly-gook of machine code, so preventing that person from discovering how the program works and then tampering with it.

Julian had "compiled" his program. To find out what the program was designed to do, we needed his original "source" code.

"Shit," said Warren working down the screen with a finger. "Here it is, but there are bits of it in files all over the place."

Julian had squirrelled bits of the program's source codes in a number of separate files which we had to draw together, open and check. The program was not a large one but it took time. One file produced a result. It listed two blocks of crucial instructions. One set informed the computer to direct a message to the computer screen every three-hundredths of a second. The other directed it to a data file where that message was stored. We found the data file and opened it up. It contained one phrase:

FORGET THE KEY.

That couldn't have meant anything to Warren, but it certainly meant something to me.

"Screen dump, Warren," I said coldly, and with eyebrows raised he obeyed.

The printer clicked into action with a carriage return, and began to reproduce the information that was being directed to the computer screen. I stood up and leaned over the paper stepping up over the platen. The first line read "FORGET THE KEY". The message must have been on the screen, but we couldn't see it. At that speed of repetition, how could we? A message displayed every three-hundredths of a second was subliminal, invisible to the naked eye, but nevertheless capable of insinuating itself into the subconsciousness. That explained why Julian had suffocated in his mask – and his missed flight to California.

"This is all a bit stupid, isn't it?" Warren said hesitantly, peering up with a worried look at my pinched face.

"Let's take out the decimal point. Make it 3.0 seconds, instead of 0.03. Let's see it."

Warren stopped the program, made the simple change to the source code, recompiled the program, and ran it.

I pinched the bridge of my nose with one hand and closed my eyes tightly. With a long sigh, I began explaining how Julian had really died. Warren didn't say a word.

It was 3.00 am, the lowest point of darkness, and Warren and I sat morosely in Julian's study hardly wanting to believe what we now knew to be true.

I was tired and began to cry, so Warren took off his shoe and picked out a silver package.

"The papers and smokes are in my jacket, babe. Let's roll."

I only ever smoked marijuana with Warren. It seemed innocent and oldfashioned compared to what you could sniff and swallow at the nicest parties nowadays.

He made some coffee while I slowly rolled and lit a joint. The pungent smell drifted in the small room like the perfume of a passing shade, and I drew in the blue smoke from the smouldering brown resin until it burned my lungs and sent a cool tingling down my arms to the tips of my fingers. I sat back quietly as Warren took the joint from me. We both sat back and watched.

One and, two and, three and. . .

    FORGET THE KEY, the green letters said.

One and, two and three and. . .

    FORGET THE KEY.

One and, two and three and. . .

    FORGET THE KEY.

It was mesmerising even at that speed.

We'd found a new twist to the old tale of murder in a quiet English village. The computer did it. The computer had killed my cousin.

CHAPTER FIVE

WE DIDN'T TELL ANNE WHAT we had found. Warren seemed to think that the message was a prank that had gone wrong; that someone at the pizza house knew Julian's taste in sex and had fooled around with his program. Barnaby had said that the new company had been interested in programs to help people lose weight; perhaps Julian had been testing the program on himself with a message saying "eat less food" and hadn't checked the message every time he logged on. The explanation made sense, but I had a bad feeling about it which kept making me dream of death with malice aforethought. First, I got depressed, and then vengeful, while in the meantime my news buds were going crazy. The weekend ended with Warren telling me I hadn't been much comfort to Anne with my nose in a glass for most of the time.

I couldn't have picked a worse time for a personal crisis. Since Thursday night I hadn't seen a paper or heard a news bulletin, so by the time I arrived at the office early on Monday morning I felt like a soldier returning to a blitzed homeland. While we had been sheltering in a quiet Hertfordshire hamlet, diverting ourselves with the penetration and exploration of someone else's computer, the world had experienced the biggest stock-market crash since 1929.

The shrieking hyperbolic headlines on the rush-hour tabloids said it all. On the day we had set off from London, £120 billion had been wiped off the value of shares quoted on the Stock Exchange. Wall Street had collapsed because of fears for the state of the US economy; the dollar was dropping like a lead ball. The currency markets were being sucked down in a menacing vortex, and with confidence in the US economy evaporating by the hour, the prognosis for world trade was grim. The longest bull market of all time had come to an end with a very big bang indeed. Screaming SELL, SELL, SELL, the brash young protagonists in the game of global dealing had been introduced to Big Daddy Bear, who had cuffed them about the ears, roughed them up and, finally, tossed the whole board in the air, scattering their pathetic pieces all around.

The markets were in free fall. The FT 100 had fallen from 2200 to 1800, the Dow Jones had plunged from 2500 to 1900, the Nikkei Dow was down from 26000 to 21000, and the Hang Seng had sunk so far that dealings in Hong Kong were suspended.

The blame was being spattered around like pudding flying from a baby's spoon. The US was being chastised for the size of its twin Budget and Trade deficits, the receipt for which totalled $300 billion a year. Treasury ministers of the major industrialised countries bawled at each other across the continents, openly accusing each other of excacerbating the world's problems with high interest rates and second-rate growth. Investors had glimpsed the nightmare of a recession and had acted accordingly.

The leading investment adviser on Wall Street, Pete Rechter, had broken first, when the September figures came through, and had printed SELL in 72-point banner headlines across his newsletter. From then on there was a rapid baton change of panic across the world's time-zones, thanks to the 24-hour globalisation of its foreign-exchange, securities and futures markets. Massive institutional investors proved no more calm than small private investors, who had stampeded to the edge of the cliff in 1929. The pension funds, which had poured billions into the world stock-markets and fuelled the bloated prices on the dealers' screens, chased the markets down the chasm.

Computerised dealing added speed to the disaster. Computer programs, with their built-in signals for when to buy and when to sell, were blamed as if they had somehow taken control from out of the safe hands of the market regulators. It had been a triple witching hour on Wall

43

Street, the Halloween of all time, when a whole quarter of stock futures and options contracts expired at once. The game of stock index arbitrage had stopped while the players totted up their profit and loss from the difference between the price of stock index futures and the value of the underlying stock. The computers had cranked out the complicated formula for success, involving options on the stock indexes as well as options on the shares. This time, as traders sought to unwind their positions, the stock-market had taken a deep dive.

Charlie East's face was as white as bookies' chalk when I pushed through the doors of *Technology Week* into an unprecedented buzz of activity. Standard Mondays usually saw journalists and salesmen dragging themselves in through the doors all through the morning, and the pace of the paper never started to quicken until Wednesday morning, or Tuesday afternoon at the earliest. That day, Max was already into a briefing session with the City staff, and he waved me over.

"Georgina, stop work on the post-Big Bang feature for the moment. I want you on this story," he said, as I joined the small group of people gathered around his desk, and then he continued, counting out on his fingers, "Four things. Overview of crash – City desk. The electronic sector, what's happening – City desk. The impact of computer trading systems, feature – Georgina. Forward bookings situation, news analysis – Mary Stow. Crash will lead as extra. OK? Other stories run."

I had only caught the tail-end of the briefing but I gathered that there had been rescheduling of the news roster. Mary, a new reporter on the news team, and I, had been pulled in to help the City team, which comprised Rupert Day, the City editor, and Charlie East. This was to be in addition to any current stories we were handling; after all, *Technology Week* was a computer industry newspaper not a financial sheet. To my dismay, my feature deadline had been pulled forward dramatically.

When Max had finished I spoke up. "Couldn't mine hold over until next week?" I said as casually as I could, with my heart threatening to burst through my coat. My neck was firmly stuck out in the path of a well-sharpened guillotine, but I was desperate. The crash was a disaster, of course, but an impersonal one nonetheless, and I wanted someone else to deal with it because I intended to use any spare time I had on tracing Lifestyle Software and the mocking murderer who had left that deadly message on the pizza house's computer. Unaware of my motives, the team stood in appalled silence, and Max looked steadily up at me, narrowing his disconcerting eyes.

"Why?"

"The nationals have already described how the computers operated. People are already blaming the machines for the crash. The story's gone. We only need a short news story on what actually happened, because the nationals won't have included much detail, and an analytical piece based on some good interviews which I can set up this week. But the market is still diving, and something might happen at the end of the week, or the beginning of next, on settlement day. Will the computers cope with that and which securities houses are going to go down the pan? We should be looking at the next story now, as well as analysing this one."

It was so sharp and spontaneous that I amazed myself. The appalled silence blew gently out into a respectful hush. Rupert and Charlie looked at their notebooks, while Max chewed the inside of his mouth. They knew that he knew that they should have drawn his attention to settlement day, but, as it transpired, Charlie had good reason to want to forget about it.

"OK, good, but do the analysis for this week and try and get a feel for who is not going to be looking forward to settlement day. We can run it this week. Right, everyone, get on with it," he said and nodded – his usual signal for the end of a meeting.

We all stood quite still for a moment, like delayed-action automatons. I could have kicked myself. He didn't look up again and we made our way briskly to our desks. As I headed for mine, Charlie caught my arm.

"Nice one, Georgie, but he's a bastard, isn't he?"

I was too annoyed to answer, but Charlie kept hold of my arm.

"I've got bad news, I'm afraid," he said with embarrassment. He had the desperate air of a young man who'd sworn to bet only his shirt and finally lost his skin. His face was unhealthily pale and his tired eyes were underscored with dark bruised smudges.

"What's the story?" I said, rather brusquely, anticipating another disappointment.

"When the shit hit the fan on Friday, I was right in front of it, George. We can forget the £750 divvy-up – that went in the rapids on Friday. So did the original stake. I blew it. It's all gone. I'm really sorry."

That meant that I had lost £1500, which in turn meant Charlie had lost at least £7500 of the club's money. Though it was a lot of money, it was only money, and I was quite relieved. I shrugged my shoulders; it had been a gamble after all.

"C'mon, Charlie, give yourself a break. I'd forgotten I had the money. Has anyone else given you a hard time over this?" I was hoping to ease his conscience and get away to my desk.

"No, no . . . but I feel really bad about it, really I do. Anyway, bad as it is, it's not the real sickener. I feel terrible about you guys, but I'm in deep myself. I swear that Max knows and is just waiting for the right time to wheel-spin my ass down those stairs."

"Believe me, Charlie, if Max knew for sure about the club, he wouldn't wait." I patted his arm sympathetically and turned to go, but he gripped my hand.

"You don't understand, George. I'm finished." As he spoke, his pale chinless face was contorted with unshed tears. "I've lost . . . £50,000."

I winced.

"Shit, Charlie. You mean not just paper – real money?"

He paused to control his emotions, but his voice trembled noticeably.

"It peaked and dived miles too soon. Everything said

46

'buy' for this stock but the stupid bastards sold. . .everything said 'buy', but they sold. The bastards all started to panic and sell. It wasn't on to sell. I took up a boatload in electronics. I knew for sure – *for sure*, I'm telling you – that they were guaranteed to go up. They were bid stock, I couldn't lose, so I had to borrow money to buy the stock. It was a dead cert. When the first dip came I though it was just a small correction, but before I knew it Wall Street crumbled and the whole fucking mountain began to slide. The broker couldn't shift it fast enough, and in the end he sold at nothing. Now I've got to settle at the price I bought it. I haven't got it, George. I just haven't got it."

Charlie had been risking our cash by trading in the account: a two-week stretch when you can buy and sell shares without putting down the cash, and you pay only one set of broker's commission. The rules are simple: buy and then sell at a profit, and on settlement day your broker writes you a cheque; buy and then sell at a loss, and you write him one. You need good information, precise timing, iron-clad nerves, and a change of underwear to play that tricky short-term dealing game. More importantly, you need a spare tea-chest full of cash just in case things go wrong. Charlie had bet money he did not have, because he thought he had had a peek at the cards – but the game had been loaded against him. It had been a three-card trick, with Charlie as the mug.

The boiling bull market with its endlessly rising prices, together with Charlie's timely acquisition of company information, had created a naive confidence in his L-plate trading skills. He was hooked to success, and he had just discovered what it was like to spill a fix and still have to pay the dealer.

He stood before me like all chastised child, tall, lanky, dark eyed and miserable, his misfortune too enormous for words of comfort to salve, and I could find none anyway. We stood for a moment in glum silence, until he gave a small tight grin and squeezed my hand again before loping off to his desk across the room from mine. As I watched his tall, hunched frame, I noticed Max watching, too, and I turned quickly away.

At my desk I was almost immobilised by so many thoughts requiring action competing for limited resources in my tired bruised brain. There was so much to do. There was an extra news story, plus the feature, and I needed to check out the facts concerning Lifestyle with Barnaby Page at Hitec first, and then with Dunan Bradley International, an organisation which held details on approximately one million public, private and government-owned companies worldwide. The latter posed a problem because my contact at Dunan's was Celia Stevenson, my friend and Eddie's – aka the special co-respondent in our divorce case. I reckoned that if I could sit on my pride, and if she didn't know about my plans to name her in court, she couldn't refuse me this tiny favour. After all, she owed me for all the trouble she had caused.

There was a yellow gummed notelet stuck above my screen, my eyes kept coming back to it as I logged on. So I paused and called my solicitor to arrange for the divorce summons to be sent direct to me so I could stuff it into Eddie's elegant pockets myself. The solicitor asked me how much my errant husband earned, but I hadn't a clue. Then I remembered Anne's words at the cottage – about Eddie's fantastic salary.

"£50,000," I replied, pulling from the air the unluckiest number around at the time.

He was impressed and his voice brightened. "And you say he works in the City, Mrs Powers?" he queried,

"He's a dealer, I believe," I said, cheered immeasurably by the hope that, for once, Eddie might have been on the losing side of a bargain, thanks to the market crash and my petition for divorce.

When we'd finished speaking, I checked my mail. There was nothing from Barnaby Page, so I telephoned him, too. His classy secretary replied, but said he was not available. She later repeated the same message with equal equanimity all morning, and he returned none of my calls. Given the events at the weekend, and my more

48

than cordial relationship with Barnaby, I could not help feeling he had been got at. Julian's connections with Lifestyle Software were apparently being systematically eradicated, and I began to suspect that whoever was fixing this had already reached Hitec. It was hard not to jump to conclusions.

My last call before lunch was to Des Pritchard, the manager of information services at Broadwick & Klein, one of the largest brokers in the City. He was a good contact I had made about two years ago when he was in charge of a major pharmaceutical company's computer installation. *Technology Week* had run a prestigious feature, with my by-line, about the installation of his firm's dealing rooms a year ago. It had been a good piece, and had gained him a few gold stars with Broadwick at the time. That day he seemed reluctant to talk.

"Georgina, I'm not really sure whether our firm would think it appropriate to be involved in this sort of analysis at this time. Our equipment – how shall I put it – is being severely tested."

"Broadwick lost big then, I take it . . ."

"Oh, no, our bonuses are safe I think. . ."

"Oh, really? So what's the problem?"

"No problem."

"Come on, Des, that's a good story for me and for you. If Broadwick didn't dive-bomb with the rest, and the computer kit help up, where's the harm in the story? The kit did hold up, didn't it?"

"I'm glad to say it did hold up, although the number of transactions was incredible. We had a few blips. Then we had a problem with some market-makers hiding behind the screens." He allowed himself a little chuckle.

"I can't see that Broadwick would mind that news getting out. It might be unseemly to gloat over others' misfortune, but wouldn't Broadwick really be rather pleased to let people know that it survived virtually unscathed, perhaps even in profit? I tell you, Des, it would be a real favour – we could do with some glitter on page this week among all this sackcloth and ashes stuff."

The flannel seemed to raise his confidence, and had massaged his ego sufficiently to get me an entrée. He wanted to impress his peer group again, perhaps even feature with a photograph – colour, of course, and dynamically bloated with the help of a fish-eye lens.

"Well, I'd have to check. They were quite pleased with the stuff you did on us last time, but these are peculiar times, Georgina, you must understand. When do you want to come in?"

"Like yesterday?" I replied, absorbing his condescension with some satisfaction. In my line of work, being underestimated helps.

"Look, I'll try and get you in as soon as I can, but the market is still on the slide, so there's pressure on me, and the dealers don't like people hanging around when they're screaming the odds. I'll have to ask the chief dealer."

"Who's that?"

"Ms Kay Fisher. Very formidable."

The name was familiar but I couldn't place it at that moment.

"Try for me, Des," I pleaded. "It's worth a good lunch."

"OK. I'll call you back."

"Today?"

"Today."

I put the receiver down and sat back. It was one o'clock, so there was no point in telephoning anyone. Charlie had already gone to the pub, but I had to get to the bank first for some cash. My budget would be breathtakingly tight now that the anticipated little bonus from the club had been trampled underfoot. I was back by ten to two, with a slice of pizza and a cinnamon-dusted custard pie, preparing the conversation with Celia in my head.

I checked my mail while dialling her number. There was nothing from Barnaby, but Warren had left a message for me to meet him that evening.

Celia's flabbergasted voice answered a few seconds after her secretary announced me.

"George?"

50

"Yes. Hello . . ." The quickfire hand-over-the-goods conversation I had planned refused to venture out to be tested.

"George?" The awkward silence had made her wonder if I was still there.

"Yes. Hello." My throat had swollen with emotion and I could barely make another sound.

"George? Are you all right?" she sounded genuinely concerned, and that helped, even though I knew I could never trust her voice again.

"Yes. Sorry. How are you?"

"Fine, fine. Well, you know, chugging along. How are you?"

"I'm okay. Well, the family had a bit of bad news. Julian's dead."

She said she was shocked and terribly sorry with such enthusiasm and concern that I guessed she was trying make up for more than my cousin's death. The fact that she didn't know about the death meant she wasn't still with Eddie, otherwise he would have told her. She began to ask me about the rest of the family but I interrupted her.

"Listen, can you do me a favour?"

"Of course," she replied with sombre intensity.

"Check out this firm. It's a brand-new software outfit based in Northern California. I need to check it out but I can't get through. I need the usual: capitalisation, investors, whether it's public or private, its directors, and so forth."

"Will do. When do you need it by?"

"ASAP."

"OK. I'll get on with it," she replied, and then after a pause said, "Look, George, why don't we meet up. It's been a long time, and everything. It might be good, for both of us. . ."

"Um, it might be. . . but I can't talk anymore right now. Look, I've got to go . . . Get back to me soon as you can. We'll talk then."

The rage in me seemed to burn from my diaphragm up across my chest, and I dropped the receiver like a hot iron. I had planned such a revenge for that girl. In the past two years, she had become even more devious, more loathsome, and more treacherous than when I had seen her sharp, shocked face behind Eddie's naked shoulder in my bed that memorable night. I had murdered her a thousand times since in a replay of the scene, where I entered and wrought my bloody revenge. The reality had been less satisfactory, for me. I had stood there, mute, emasculated, the blood draining from my face, my hand at my mouth. After a bloated moment of shock, they had jumped up, baring their wet stomachs and pink pressed flesh – as I ran from the room. Sitting downstairs in our Clapham maisonette, I could hear her tiny hurrying feet pattering from chair to chair gathering up her expensive clothes. But I never remembered her clothed again – I remembered only her fat ankles and swinging breasts. When she had gone, Eddie held my waist while I vomited in the sink. "Forgive me, babe," he had said. "Forgive me." But I never did.

The memory of his guilty voice faded as a call came through for me. It was Des Pritchard, and he'd arranged for me to visit Broadwick's at 9.00 am the next day. I jotted it in my diary and put it on screen for entry in the office's electronic diary.

Then I made a couple more calls about stories I was scheduled for on the news roster, and that finished, I opened up a file onscreen, cleared a space for my notebook amongst the debris on my desk, and began to write. It was seven by the time I had finished, but the office was still busy. Charlie was sitting glumly by his desk, shuffling some paper, and I offered to buy him a pint at the Crown. It was eleven by the time we lurched home.

Max had arranged for Nick Weston, a freelance photographer, to meet me outside the offices of Broadwick & Klein, one of the most prestigious brokerages in the City of London. It was a cold, bright autumnal morning and the sun glinted off the bronze-mirrored double-glazed windows and the deep dark slabs of marble supporting the self-important portals of the lofty building in Bishopsgate. I waited impatiently for Nick outside. I wanted this to be a quick in-and-out job so I could get on with other work I had planned. Nick's stocky frame appeared dead on time, carrying an aluminium case and with a copy of *Private Eye* protruding from an inside pocket of his oversized jacket. He stopped momentarily to drop the stub of a cigarette and grind it into the ground.

We pushed through the vast, heavy glass doors, breezing into the building together like litter from the street. We stopped at the edge of a grey marbled floor shaped like a dollar sign, which curved first towards an oval matt-black reception desk and then into a glass-tube lift which pumped silently up and down bearing slick-haired sharp-suited men and an occasional power-dressed, pinstriped woman. A red-haired, creamy-skinned receptionist, flanked by two inscrutable black security guards, delivered a pre-set crimson smile of greeting before curling her matching diamond-cut nails around the telephone receiver to announce our arrival.

"Mr Pritchard will be ready in about five minutes. He will send someone down for you." Another crimson smile, highlighted by light green disinterested eyes, then she looked down at her keyboard to enter the date and time. With two sharp clicks, two visitors's passes were placed the matt-black surface of the desk, and her hand waved us beyond an exquisite Bonsai willow towards a sumptious array of black leather seating curving around the window walls.

We picked up our passes and walked thirty feet to a long settee. A *Financial Times* lay pristine, pink and unopened on a low white marble coffee table. The headlines declared that the situation in the world stock markets would get worse before it would get better. The financial ministers in the Group of Seven were still haranguing each other, the stock market indicators had fallen yet again overnight, and the City was bracing itself for another steep slide.

"Pretty bad." I said to Nick, pointing at the newspaper.

"Dunno, and don't care," he replied, squinting into a

lens he'd pulled from his case, and sticking out his stubbled jaw while he chewed at his top lip. "Up or down, we'll still be grubbing around."

"Oh," I said, slumping back into the soft leather and contemplating the true value of our reporting and discussing major events at all.

The tubular elevator sank quietly to the floor and a shirtsleeved Des Pritchard, wearing square blue-framed glasses, appeared. He came towards us with long gangling strides, his pale hand outstretched. I already knew he wouldn't have sent his secretary, because he chose to project the image of a data-processing department with a personal touch. Some computer folk are sensitive to such pretentions.

"Ah, Des! Hello!" I said, warmly, my stomach muscles struggling to flex me out from the depths of the settee. Eventually, Des and Nick were able to heave me out, and we were all laughing by the time I made the introductions.

"Shall we?" Des grinned and extended his long bony arm towards the glass tube. The cuffs of his handmade shirt were fastened by smooth lozenges of gold. There was no such sartorial finesse when he had been in pharmaceuticals and when chemical dust, not money, was the product.

We crossed the shiny floor to be enfolded within the silent elevator and drawn skywards. As the marbled floors slipped by like clouds, we watched walkways spiral into rooms, and rooms spin into reception areas strategically greened with leafy potted plants as high as trees and fed by silent waterfalls. Within seconds we arrived at the fourth floor, and we crossed another glossy marble expanse to the steely doors of the data-processing department. Des pushed one of them open and led us into his office.

It was a large windowless room decorated in shades of green and furnished with a broad L-shaped teak desk, two upmarket office chairs in front of it and a large, tweed high-backed swivel-chair behind. On the wall facing his desk hung three maps indicating the time-zones and the major markets in foreign exchange, securities and futures – Broadwick & Klein dealt in them all. Five clocks hung above, set to the times of New York, London, Hong Kong, Tokyo and Sydney. On his desk were three internal telephones distinguishable by different-coloured lights, one full-featured digital telephone, which could handle external calls, and a personal computer.

Des picked up one of the internal phones and ordered coffee while Nick opened his case and set up his tripod to take a few shots of the tall balding man behind his desk. I began to ask questions about the computer systems which handled the dealing rooms and those which handled the back-office settlements. Des reached for a button under his desk and pressed it. The wall behind peeled silently away, and through the reinforced glass window a cavernous grey room came into view.

We stood and looked down. Directly below was a curved bank of wedge-shaped terminals which monitored eight central processing units lined up in cool grey lines towards the back of the room. On the right was a bank of tape and disk drives behind which was a sectioned-off, glass-screened tape library containing banks of steel tins and a row of five matrix and laser printers. Beyond the tape library was another sealed room, which Des said housed another four minicomputers and a selection of personal computers for development work. The whole department was manned by approximately thirteen operators. There were three individual offices for the resident engineers provided by the computer manufacturers, because when its computer systems went down, Broadwick did not want to wait for a second longer than it had to for repairs. Spread before us was easily five million pounds' worth of equipment, without counting the secret back-up facilities shadowing the systems here from a basement two streets away.

The bulk of this equipment had been installed a year ago, in preparation for the deregulation of the Stock Exchange. Broadwick, and firms like it, had invested millions to automate their market-making and trading operations in preparation for the ferocious competition expected from the international financial organisations who operate twenty-four hours a day around the world.

Information, lightning reactions, and bulk trading were the key to survival in this hostile environment, and Broadwick had made sure it would not be found lacking in any department.

Des pressed another button under his desk, and an automatic blind on the wall opposite the door rolled quietly away to reveal a dealing room half the size of a football pitch. Strip downlights bathed it in a lugubrious synthetic glow. Some fifty shirt-sleeved dealers sat amid a jumble of equipment and untidy towers of paper, six screens per man – there were five women that I could see – and at least two telephones each, not counting the portables.

Numerous heavy screens hung from the suspended ceilings to display current prices, just in case someone happened to look away from the screen on his desk and missed something. Each dealer had a range of market intelligence services, such as the Reuters, Telerate and the Stock Exchange's TOPIC and EPIC share prices and market indices services at his fingertips.

The screens which display this information are controlled by computerised "switches" which channel information, in video form, along leased lines, from the information suppliers. Dealers haven't got time to dial them up. Information must be piped in all the time.

Thanks to the deregulation and automation of the Stock Exchange and the computerised Stock Exchange Quotations System (SEAQ) introduced in London in 1986, dealing can take place away from the Stock Exchange floor. Market makers, such as Broadwick & Klein use their terminals to enter two-way prices for the SEAQ stocks in which they are registered, and to report their trades.

The Stock Exchange computers report the best bid and ask prices, or in the case of Alpha securities – the most actively traded stock – the last trade information, and feed it back to the market makers and dealers.

Other computers calculate a range of stock-market

indices, including the important *Financial Times* Stock Exchange 100, or Footsie, by taking information from SEAQ and the traded options market.

Broadwick's computers were also linked directly into the Stock Exchange information services, in order to receive the data in a raw digital form. They could then store the information, work on it and present it in any way the organisation required. For example, the computers could combine information on certain stocks with Broadwick's own analysts' evaluations.

Broadwick's computers tracked all its dealers' trades and arranged the settlements at the end of each two-week trading account, before co-operating with the Stock Exchange's central settlement system, Talisman.

Nick, impressed by the gadgetry, made a couple of uncharacteristically inquisitive and enthusiastic remarks, until I froze him out with a hard stare. The last thing I wanted was the interview being diverted or, worse still, extended. Max was going to get a plain story of computers making good under extreme pressure, and I didn't want it to last the whole morning.

I pointed out to Des that the problem every broker and banker would be facing on settlement day would be the sheer turnover of sales. The newspapers had reported that selling had achieved such volumes on Friday that the link between TOPIC and EPIC had collapsed temporarily, so that the display of price information was suspended. Des shrugged, then produced some statistics on the volume of transactions with a couple of taps at his PC.

There had been an amazing four thousand transactions recorded. After glancing through them, I stared out on to the dealing room again. I had never seen a dealing room "live". My experience, until then, had been entirely vicarious, fed only by television news stills and the occasional pan of a camera across wildy waving individuals in order to illustrate some late-night money or property programme.

Given the desperate state of the markets, I had expected to see a good deal more activity in Broadwick's than was apparent that day. A few of the dealers were grouped around one screen, watching the prices slide, like disinterested holidaymakers watching a swimmer wave and drown. No one had so much as broken into a sweat or loosened a tie. Then I noticed a small auburn-haired woman in a powder-blue suit striding purposefully between the desks. I thought I recognised her.

"Who's she?" I asked.

"Oh, that's Kay Fisher, the chief dealer. It's thanks to her that Broadwick & Klein got out of a lot of stocks when it did, and is exercising favourable options now, to boot. She's quite brilliant, resourceful. . . and forceful."

"I've seen her somewhere before."

"Oh, she was on the television not long ago. Flavour of the month for the press," he answered smugly.

"Oh, yes?" I said, and the memory of her nodding, smiling head on the evening news, the day Julian died, presented itself on cue. I didn't look back at Des, but his last remark had not gone unnoticed. He was displaying the sort of nonchalance towards us that is commonplace amongst those who have only ever had to present a good story to a journalist, often with the help of some public relations officer. For them the mad media dog soon metamorphosises into a domesticated slipper-warmer which will come at the click of a finger, a low whistle, or the tug of a leash. No helpful PR interface was on hand today, which meant that Des had acquired a certain confidence in his own media-handling ability since we last met.

"I'd like a picture of her standing by a dealer's desk," said Nick, dismantling his tripod, packing it quickly, and getting ready to drive through the window of opportunity that had presented itself.

"Well. . . I don't know. She really has nothing to do with the computer side of it." Des gazed anxiously down at her and thrust his hands into his striped pockets, pulling them forward while rising and lowering quickly up and down on his toes.

"But she *uses* them doesn't she, Des?" I said, looking

out over the dealing room. "Can you take us down? Show us your service to the shop floor, so to speak? I mean, she must have used whatever information you delivered to good effect on Friday."

"Well. . . it is rather difficult. She's rather busy."

His tall thin body was rocking back and forth from heel to toe, moving up and down more quickly now. It was plain that he had not fully discussed our visit with either the chief dealer or Broadwick's public relations department, so anxious had he been to appear all covered in glory on the cover of *Technology Week*.

Nick opened the door and I followed him instantly. Des darted from the window, anxiously pushing himself in front of us to try and guide and control our passage down some spiral stairs which led to the level of the dealing room. He leaned on a set of double doors and we entered the large, airless dealing room. It had a stale reek of old tobacco, aftershave, and sour body odour. What activity there was ceased for a moment, and some joker whistled long and hard – at me I presumed, but it could have been at Nick, whose dark bohemian looks should have directed him to a career in front of the camera instead of behind it.

Des was obviously embarrassed. If it had been a busier day no one would have noticed us at all, and even on this quiet morning we were worth only a minute's surveillance. We stood together for that minute, and then Nick made off to introduce himself to a couple of dealers. He wanted some good close-ups of the screens showing red as the prices plummeted. Des looked desperately after him like a scout-master having lost one of his troop. I looked across the desks for Kay Fisher, and spotted her leaning over a desk to talk to a dealer.

"There she is, over there," I said.

"She looks rather busy," Des replied hopelessly.

"Well, if that's so, she's the only person in here who is," I retorted, starting to move. "Let's go over and see what's going on."

I raised my hand to Nick and pointed over the desks.

We both made our respective ways over to her, with Des muttering anxiously behind me.

"Well, well, well," I said quietly when we at last stood facing her behind the dealer's shiny dark head. "If it isn't whatisname."

Kay Fisher straightened, coolly raising a fine eyebrow, her delicate hand fingering a string of pearls around her white neck. Eddie turned quickly to face me, and his look of surprise gave way instantly to a broad, perfect smile. He stood up and took my shoulders, and I stiffened as he bent over to kiss my cheek. Then he turned to Ms Fisher, whose face was set in an expression of indifference, and placed an avuncular hand on her back. It was a totally inappropriate display of familiarity towards someone of her seniority, but Eddie liked to play that sort of game. His actions were transparent to me now. If he had been just another jock in her department, he would have soon lost that arm at the elbow. But he obviously wasn't – and his little gesture was a clear message for me. She didn't move a muscle until he delivered his malevolent gift to her.

"Kay, this is my wife. Georgina, this is Kay Fisher." Good to see you, Georgina."

His introduction prompted a sting of a smile on her face so sour it tingled the fillings in my teeth. She proffered her small, cold, perfectly manicured alabaster hand for me to shake, and we limply tugged at each other's fingertips for little more than a second.

"Pleased to meet you," she nodded, her mouth upturned in a vestigial smile, and then, turning steelily to Eddie, she said, "I must go now. I'll talk to you later."

"Oh, do wait, Miss Fisher. It's you I wish to speak to. I'm here from *Technology Week*, a computer industry newspaper. We're doing a story on Broadwick & Klein's computer system: how it survived the crash and how its settlements are going to shape up. I believe that Broadwick did rather well, thanks to you."

She stood quite still and looked directly at Des Pritchard, who stood sweating uncomfortably by my shoulder.

"On whose invitation are you here?"

"Broadwick's press office thought it would be a good story," I said, giving Des a break.

"Ah," she said ominously, then she turned to me and smiled almost warmly.

"In that case, Mrs Powers, why don't you come over to my desk and I'll show you how we make money round here."

"Thanks very much," I said, letting Nick and Des follow her while I hung back to speak to Eddie who was beckoning. "George, I'm really sorry about Julian. It was a terrible shock." His deep brown-lashed eyed seemed filled with concern and emotion.

"Yes, it was a shock."

"He'd just come good, too, with that job in California. What a bummer."

"What do you know about it, Eddie?"

"The job?"

"Yes, the job."

"Oh, he didn't say much. It was just the luckiest break he'd ever had. It was some great set-up to write new software for the mass market."

"How come they chose Julian, then?"

"I don't know. He worked for a pizza place, didn't he?"

"Exactly."

Eddie folded his arms across his broad chest and looked down at me with the sort of tolerant amused smiled that people reserve for the efforts and opinions of adolescents.

"Now what are you getting at, George?"

"I just think it's a bit odd that his firm picked him from nowhere to work on some great project. It might be an interesting story for us. Did he tell you anything about the company?"

He feigned a look of distaste. "Jeez, George, you won't pass up a chance of a story, no matter how it comes. Hell no, not much. I don't think he trusted me. I don't blame him either. It was a very tempting deal there."

It was quite likely that Julian would have been cautious

enough not to tell Eddie, even though they were close friends. Eddie was an incorrigible opportunist, which, of course, was part of his attractiveness.

"Why did you call?" I said, changing the subject and looking over at Kay Fisher's desk.

She was sitting on it, her perfect legs crossed and her back to the screens, as Nick worked around her. The activity in the office was gathering momentum. The dealers were beginning to snap and snarl into their telephones and press at matrices on their screens.

"Just wanted to talk. . . about things," he said so softly that I could scarcely hear him above the noise, even if I had intended to listen. I reached into my shoulder-bag for a long brown envelope that had arrived in the early-morning post, and Eddie's eyes hardened as I tucked it into his top pocket and patted his chest.

"This is for you, sweetie. It's a summons . . . for our divorce. See you in court."

I smiled, stepped back from him, and with a coquettish wave of my hand moved off to join the others.

Kay Fisher gave me ten minutes of her valuable time, then showed us the door.

Outside, the traffic was jamming up along Bishopsgate thanks to the building work extending around Liverpool Street station. But, despite the fumes and grime, the air was fresh by comparison to the cramped dealing room between Broadwick's marbled floors. The sound of drills and pile-drivers billowed out from under the tarpaulins and scaffolding that shield pedestrians from the base rubble and dust being transformed into another palace of offices for yet another financial empire to dwell in the City.

"I wouldn't give a shit for that poor pratt's chances," Nick yelled over the noise. He lit a cigarette and offered me one. I shook my head and scanned the busy street for a black cab for hire.

"Who?"

"Pritchard."

"Yes, well. . .he's a good data-processing guy, one of

the best. He'll survive – if not there, then somewhere else."

The sunlight was beginning to hurt my eyes. A gust of wind whipped dust into my face and a tear rolled down my cheek.

"You OK?" Nick stuck his case between his legs and took my arm. I pulled away and searched in my bag for a paper handkerchief. Nick offered me a clean white folded cotton one. It smelled of fresh laundry, of clean pressed sheets.

"Thanks. Bloody building dust. This city'll be all right when it's finished." I wiped my eyes and shielded them from the sun with my hand.

"Didn't know you were married, George."

"I'm trying not to be. What about you?" I said, handing back his smudged handkerchief and looking around again for a cab.

"Me? No. Look, I'm sorry, I didn't mean. . . ."

I cut his apology short by calling out "Taxi!" and raising my arm at a cab on the opposite side of the street. It stopped dead to the sound of angry horns, and we both ran through the oncoming traffic towards it.

"I need those pictures as soon as possible, Nick. It'll go front-page for sure. This firm must be the only one on the City which used its computers effectively to predict the crash and to capitalise on it at speed. In short, Broadwick & Klein made a killing," I said, without looking at him, and pressing back in the hard leather seat as the cabbie swung round and across to the other side of the street, then down a narrow alleyway.

I could feel Nick looking at me for while, then he spoke up. "Hey, you've got good skin, you know. You'd photograph pretty well."

I didn't bother to look away from the window.

"That's funny. A friend told me the other day that my skin looked disgusting."

There was a pause.

"So who do you believe?"

63

"My friend, of course."

I heard him strike a match and inhale.

"Hurt bad, eh, Georgina?"

"Hurt bad."

We didn't speak again until the taxi reached Old Compton Street. I let him pay.

CHAPTER SIX

IT WAS SIX O'CLOCK AND I'd made my last telephone call of
the day. The traffic was noisily snarling up in Old Compton
Street and every little Soho street that led into it. Street-
smart commuters were beginning to herd, window-dressing
the bright new showcase brasseries. It was getting dark
outside. I looked up at the grimy office windows which
reflected the blinking blue and pink lights of the sleazier
Brewer Street clubs. The rumble of motors and music rose
up to my window, together with the smell of dark ground
coffee, oriental cuisine and diesel fumes. I began to feel
hungry.

I decided to eat and go home to bed, but as I rose to go,
the telephone rang.

"Georgina Powers," I said wearily, stuffing the receiver
under my chin and searching for some paper and a pencil
on my desk.

"Hi, it's me."

It was Warren and, too late, I remembered his message.

"Warren, I'm so sorry I forgot to get back to you. Listen,
I've been really tied up. . ."

"Yeh, yeh."

"No really, believe me, all hell has let loose here since the
crash, and on Monday night I had to go out with Charlie
to help him drown his sorrows. He had some pretty bad
news."

"Yeh?"

It was hard work.

"Warren. . .he lost £50,000 in the crash."

"Oh dear, oh dear."

I said nothing more. Warren could be a cold bastard
sometimes.

"Can you see me tonight?" he asked.

I sighed. What I really needed was a decent burial. My eyes were heavy with terminal tiredness and, as I looked up through the haze of aerial debris above the office machines, I imagined the bliss of a few hours of lonely oblivion generated with the help of a half, possibly a full, bottle of dry white wine. Deep under a duvet, in a quiet darkened room, I would spend the night indifferent to, untroubled by what was happening in my street, my town, my city, my country, my world. Nothing and no one would be able to squeeze another fact or fiction into my head. I didn't want to communicate. I didn't want to interface. I wanted my senses unplugged, completely blanketed and still, humming "Heaven, heaven is a place, where nothing, nothing ever happens."

I need a break, God, my inner voice prayed.

"Still there?" Warren interrupted.

"Oh, sorry. . . someone was talking to me. Yes, yes of course. . . I'll meet you in about an hour and a half at home, OK?"

"Cool. OK."

I owed him, I explained to myself.

He was waiting impatiently outside my door when I got back. I unlocked it and he followed me in. The room was a little untidy, but I pretended not to notice Warren's look of distaste and went straight into the kitchen. Inevitably, he drew all of it to my attention.

"George, look at this place." He stood in the middle of the living-room, his arms outstretched, like a mortified Black Madonna.

"So what?" I replied, turning my back again and opening the refrigerator to grasp what remained of an old bottle of white wine. He came into the kitchen and took me by the arm.

"I need to talk to you, Georgina."

"What about?" I replied wearily.

"About this, about you. . ." he pointed at grubby patches in the kitchen, then through the door to the living-room, and finally jabbed a finger at me – Her Ultimate Grubbiness.

I held my hand up to stop his flow of wasted words.

"No way. You are not lecturing me tonight. You want to go out, right, we will go out, but you are not going to lecture me. I have had it. If you don't like my little rabbit hutch then go back to your own."

I stepped around him to look for a glass in my cupboard. Then I stood with my back to him, tugging irritably at the cork in the wine bottle.

"Leave it out," he said coldly, stopping my hand.

I turned slowly towards him. His face was taut with anger. Little creamy white bumps had appeared at either side of his dark, downturned mouth. We looked hard and steadily at each other, like a mongoose and a snake.

Exasperated, I tried to pull my hand away, but he tightened his cold grip.

"Don't," he said.

"What is it with you nowadays? Get off my back, will you," I said viciously. "You're not my bleeding mother. Now. . .piss off."

He stood back, his lips spreading into a tawny, pink, sarcastic grin. His tough, narrow hips were thrust forward and he rested his long hands on them.

"Nice, very nice. Quite a rebel, eh? Poor posh little cast-off, bobbing along awash with fucking booze and self-pity. Look at yourself. Look at all this . . .this shit in 'ere . . . and in 'ere." He tapped his head and stuck his dark face forward, only an inch from mine. "Don't it matter to you that this place stinks. . .stinks of your stale clothes, rotten garbage. And old booze? Don' it matter that you haven't changed or washed in days? Don' it matter? What's up? No one going to look at you and care?"

He backed off and strutted into the other room.

"You're pafetic, George."

I was wide-eyed with fury and disbelief. The answers I wanted to give would have surely come to me, but at a later, much more irrelevant date. Instead, with a voice shrill with impotence, I mimicked his mocking tone. "Pafetic, George!"

He had already turned to go, but he looked over his shoulder to utter his final poisonous delivery.

"Yeh well, I suppose your accent is all you got that's 'igh-class now, eh?"

I heard the door open and slam shut as I stood alone in the kitchen. The flat was as deathly silent as I had earlier wanted and needed it to be. I poured myself a loud glassful of wine and drew it to my lips. It was sour and, infuriated, I spat the contents of my mouth into the sink, chucking the rest and the glass splashing and splintering after it.

Clenching my fists to my temples, I yelled as loudly as I could to the grubby kitchen walls, to the old tenement and myself.

"All right! I'll have a bloody bath!"

Minutes passed quietly by before the slow laughter began in the other room. I peered in and saw Warren still standing there. He turned and, shaking his head at me, made his way to a cupboard by my bedroom to hunt for the vacuum cleaner. He found it and went into my bedroom. Embarrassed by this, I hurried after him. The curtains were still drawn from the morning, the bed was rumpled and unmade, and the laundry basket was over-flowing. The wardrobe door was open and my clothes hung there in disarray. The room seemed to represent the contents of my mind – unkempt and edging on the boundaries of control.

"'Bout time you sorted this lot out, innit?" he remarked, pointing to the laundry basket.

"What do you want me to do: separate them into whites and coloureds for you?" I replied bitterly.

"An idea, an idea," he said, ignoring my tone. Service wash don't cost hardly anyfing."

"You're so perfect, aren't you?"

"Just normal, just normal. Normal people take dirty laundry to the launderette – especially when it backs up to six weeks' worth and alien life forms move in."

I left him to it.

"I don't forgive you," I called out peevishly, walking into the bathroom and twisting the taps on.

Warren followed and stood leaning on the door frame.

"You're lucky," I said eventually. "I had a particularly good day today."

"Yeh. It sounds like it."

I folded my arms and looked at him defiantly, but my lip trembled. I couldn't understand why he kept trying to provoke me.

He reached out and touched my face with his cool hand. He always had cool hands.

"I'm sorry, babe. You think no-one cares, but . . . I do. I care about ya."

It was touching and dangerously emotional.

"I'll be all right, Warren. I'll be all right," I said, trying to stop the wave of feeling he was building.

"I didn't mean what I said," he added, breaking the new silence.

"Which bit?"

"The bit about your accent."

"That all?"

I paused, a little self-conscious, and then smiled and repeated what I'd said before.

"I did have a good day today, Warren. I got to Eddie. I done 'im like a kipper, to coin one of your phrases."

He laughed when I told him the story of how I'd tucked the summons in Eddie's pocket, but grew serious when I described the scene with Kay Fisher. I reassured him, as confidently as I could, that there was absolutely no jealousy on my part and that it really didn't hurt anymore.

He shrugged and, pushing him playfully away, I shut the bathroom door. Within minutes I heard the roar of the vacuum cleaner in another room.

While I lay peering through the steam and wiggling my toes through the sweet-smelling foam, Warren cleaned my flat. He was right. I couldn't remember when I had last washed like this in a nice deep, hot bath, lapping soapy bubbles over my breasts. I noted that they were smaller than they used to be, and even my hips, distorted as they

69

were by the water, were lean and spare. My legs were skinnier, too. I hardly recognised my own body. It was as if I was someone new.

When I'd finished I wrapped a little towel around myself, cleaned the bath, and leaned over the sink to wash my hair. It had grown long, thick, dark and shaggy. The ends were vibrant blueberry, remnants of a previous personality, a previous brainstorm. Wiping the condensation from the mirror and wondering if I should have it cut, I noticed that, though my cheeks were rosy, my face was quite thin, its blue eyes too deep-set. Two frown marks were slightly visible over the slight hook of my nose. I rubbed fretfully at them with my hand, pulling my hair back at the same time to smooth my forehead. Resignedly, I let my damp hair fall like ropes about my face and started to move back. In a moment of dizziness, the image in the mirror dissolved. The room seemed to tilt as my stomach lurched with nausea. Looking down, I tried to steady myself at the washbasin, but I couldn't stop myself falling. I called out into the blankness, and when I opened eyes, Warren was lifting me from the floor.

"Bad circulation and an empty stomach," he said reassuringly, covering my undignified nakedness as best he could as I sat, where he'd placed me, on the toilet seat with my head wedged between my knees. After a few minutes, I looked up and self-consciously tried to apologise as he ran a flannel under the cold tap and squatted down to dab my bruised temple. Warren had handled my unconscious nude form more times than any man alive. If he'd wanted to flirt with necrophilia, I'd have been in big trouble by now.

I made noises about staying in for the evening, but Warren would have none of it. He turned on the blow-heater in the bedroom, dragged a baggy cream silk shirt and a short black skirt from the wardrobe, and forced me to dress up. When I teetered out of the door in my spiky high heels, I took his arm affectionately.

"You're beautiful, babe," he laughed, tickling me into the lift.

We went to a steakhouse in Bethnal Green and I ate fish. It was the sort of place where East End villains took their molls. Every man wore an Armani-style suit or, at the very least, soft roll-necked cashmere and leather. The women tended towards tight skirts and Bardot tops scooped off their brown, sunbedded shoulders spiked by myriad gelled ends of highlighted hair. If a bomb had dropped on the place, it would have altered the gold price of the day. The atmosphere was rich with the reek of expensive perfume and the drifting smoke from king-sized cigarettes and charcoal-grilled T-bones. In the background the vacuous sound of bazoukia tinkled relentlessly. It was a strange choice for Warren, not least because, even in these enlightened times, the type of East Enders that surrounded us were conservative to a man about conspicuous mixed-race coupling.

"Why did you bring us here?" I whispered, once Adonis, the boyish curly-haired Greek waiter had seated us.

"You get half-decent portions," he whispered back, "lots of elbow room, and no one you know is going to come 'ere."

There was something to be said for that, I thought. While we waited for the first course, he leaned back with one arm on the back of his chair. I noticed for the first time that he'd cut his dark-brown corkscrew hair shorter. It looked glossy and sharp, gleaming in the candlelight. His white teeth glinted as he smiled widely across at me. This was more like him, I thought. My head had stopped aching, and I felt happy to be sharing the evening with him.

Warren made me eat a lot, while allowing me a modest amount to drink. I tried to talk about the weekend but he stopped me every time, directing me to something else on the menu or topping up my glass, a teasing amount each time. He didn't want to hear about Julian or Lifestyle or Charlie or Max or anything that had happened at *Technology Week*. While Adonis served us discreetly, we reminisced about places and parties we'd been to together, and promised ourselves a decent clubbing night soon. As the neighbouring pubs emptied, the restaurant became more

71

crowded, with teams of young City brokers, drowning their sorrows – barely distinguishable from the local wide boys except for the absence of their women. Even so, Warren and I remained secluded and alone in our private island of quiet companionship.

Finally we sat back with large, bulbous glasses of cognac, replete and relaxed. I watched contentedly while Warren ran a long finger thoughtfully around the rim of his glass.

"You have to lick it to get it to ring," I suggested, wetting my lips with the brandy.

He didn't answer that. He was still rubbing his finger thoughtfully around his glass.

"Georgina, I've got somefin' to tell you," he said finally, looking over at me with his enigmatic cat's eyes. Those hazel eyes may have been enigmatic, but the look was one I had seen before. I had a premonition that Warren was going to utter something that we would both regret.

"I've done a few good programming contracts recently and, what with the cab an' that, I've saved some cash, enough for a deposit and more for a house. I wanna get away. I gotta chance now to leave the flat, maybe even London . . . but I want you to come wiv me."

I must have looked like the fish I had just eaten: immobilised, my mouth agape. I had no reply.

Warren's was a totally unexpected suggestion, given our platonic, prickly-in-places relationship. He was also showing me a side of his character that had never been apparent before. It was the fresh attitude to *investment* that caught me unawares. He was a man who had always had money, and had a true old-fashioned East End approach to it. The aim was to get a wodge of it in your back pocket and spend it. If you have, you spend; if you ain't, you go out and get. A downpayment on bricks and mortar was an unthinkable encroachment on disposable income. It was too long-term. Money was about liquidity; it was about not having anyone on your back; it was about good time, freedom, materialism, consumer equality. The never-never – but never a mortgage.

Warren was covering himself with respectability and

offering me a come-on that I would have expected from a nice middle-class boy from Orpington. My mudlark had been corrupted by aspirations to join the system, to get locked in and get moving, to get upwardly mobile. He'd used all the key words: "contracts", "saved", "deposit", "house". Only the use of the word "cash" had betrayed his roots. Curiously, if he had told me he was buying outright, I would have felt less perturbed. I hid my disappointment, and playfully chided him a little.

"Warren, you haven't got a credit card, have you?"

"Patronising bitch. Make it easy, why don't you?"

I decided to take him seriously, and try and skip around what he'd wanted to say.

"You could have left any time, Warren. You've always had enough money from the cab to do that. I thought it *suited* you to live there. It's not as if the rent is unbearable, is it?" I said, encouragingly.

"It's a bleedin' dump, and you know it. I want to live somewhere better. I want *you* to live somewhere better. I can get somewhere better for us now. . . where you can live nice. . . and be happy." He leaned towards me, his hazel eyes flickering in the candlelight. Let me take you away from all this, they were saying, arousing in me those good old mixed feelings of pity and contempt. I didn't know whether to laugh or cry.

"Why are you asking me, Warren?" I replied, resting my face on my hands and smiling tolerantly.

"You need me to look after you. I care for you, Georgina, you must know that. I know what you need," he said cockily, leaning back and then draining his glass.

It was his strange, infuriating, convoluted way. Warren thought he could do me a favour while he was sorting one out for himself. He couldn't talk of his love, our mutual affection, only about care, my weakness, and a good lifestyle. My brushes with love, he knew, had been disastrous, so, to be generous to him, perhaps he was trying a different tack. Whatever, I felt more offended than flattered.

"Sure you don't want to reach over here and pat me on

73

the head? You talk to me as if I'm a moron. I choose to be the way I am; the way I am is all I can cope with. I don't want to be what someone else thinks I should be, least of all you. And I don't want to live my life in a safety harness in Casa Pupo land. Warren, if you have got something else on your mind, then get on and say it. If you want to move, then move. I'll be sorry to see you go and I'll miss you, for sure. If you want to nanny me, then your flat in Bow is as close as you're going to get. You want to take me over, checking out what I eat, what I drink, checking me in and checking me out. It's OK by me, up to a point, but don't ever forget that I can and bloody well will look after myself. We're friends now – let's keep it that way, shall we? What more do you want? Is there something more?"

There was a lot more, though I didn't know the half of it, but it didn't look like Warren was going to explain, that night. All he said was "quite a speech" before pursing his lips and paying the bill, in cash, sullenly and at speed. He always paid; that was one of his rules. We stood up in silence and he placed his hand in the small of my back and directed me out of the restaurant. For a moment – to those who cared to watch – I was his girl.

Though he'd had a couple of drinks himself, he drove us home without incident and without a word, past the remnants of stumpy terraces to our unprepossesing tenement block. Within quarter of an hour we were standing silently, side by side, in the crude lift, ablaze with hip-hop graffiti and dirty little drawings, as it cranked us up to the fifth floor. Warren always got out to see me home. That night I was glad that he did, because the door to my flat was slightly ajar and it was ominously dark inside.

We looked questioningly at each other and Warren crept slowly in front of me towards the door. My skin was goose-pimpling with fear and my feet were preparing to run. Warren held his arm out as if to prevent me rushing forward – as if I would have. Kicking the door gingerly with his foot, he gently edged it wider, feeling around the inside wall for the light switch. He flicked it on and we both lurched backwards. Nothing and no one flew out at us, but the scene of carnage, suddenly illuminated, sent our hands reaching to each other.

The room had been systematically ripped apart. There was not a single possession that was not pulled open, spilled, shattered and smashed. The furniture had been upturned, mutilated and thrown aside; the curtains hung in shreds. My desk had been hacked, and under its broken legs the dented computer lay swallowing the shards of its screen. The awful destruction was made infinitely worse by the obscene expressions of violence sprayed red and black on every single wall. There was no mistaking that the perpetrators knew a woman lived there.

"Jesus Christ," breathed Warren in stunned disbelief, and I glumly lay my chin on his shoulder. We gazed into the room for a long time before, resignedly, I pushed his arm softly away and bent over to pick up a disk that lay in the mucky debris at our feet.

"Hardly worth clearing up earlier, was it?" I remarked ruefully, counting the cigarette burns on the disk's surface and twirling it around my finger as I stepped through the broken glass to the bedroom. It, too, was wrecked, clothes had been slashed, and there was a nauseating stench of urine rising from my sodden, torn bedclothes. I looked down at a drawerful of stained underwear, and saw Julian's red and silver penknife gouging a torn picture of my cousins – Julian, Anne, Richard – with the dog and me on a hot summer holiday a long, long time ago. It was strange to see the open blade lying there.

Tears of anger ran down my cheeks as Warren led me upstairs to his flat and called the police. They came to the same conclusion as we had: since everything of obvious value lay in fragmented pieces about my flat, it was likely to be an act of vandalism rather than burglary. I couldn't give them any answers. Nothing had been insured because insurance rates were prohibitive in this block in Bow. I assured them that Warren and I were friends but they questioned him closely all the same. Neither of us mentioned to them the seemingly unconnected events that had occurred in the past week.

When they had gone I sat on the floor, warming myself by the gas fire, and tried to reconcile the gut feeling I had with logic. My instincts told me that I had trodden on someone's toes, but my brain reasoned that it was surely only a matter of time before my flat—or anyone else's in this block—got the treatment. I just couldn't comprehend the sheer scale and venom of it and, as the possibilities ran through my mind, Warren made a statement that tipped the scales against reason.

"I think you should lay off nosing around. Someone don't want you stirring up this Lifestyle thing, for sure," he said, handing me a mug of coffee.

"You think it's them? Funny, so do I," I mused. "But why all this right now? I haven't got close to any answers yet. And I haven't got close to anyone."

Warren took two joints from the pocket of his jacket, which hung over a chair. He threw one in my lap. I left it and leaned back against the cool leather of his sofa as he lay down flat on the grey carpeted floor, looking at the ceiling, his arms behind his head, his ankle-booted feet crossed.

"Yeh, but they've got close to you. Lay off, George. I reckon that your cousin's death was a mistake – I do. He was into something that someone serious don' want you to know about. You were lucky you were out tonight. Fink about it. And fink about my offer."

"Some offer," I said rudely.

He turned over and leaned up on his elbow.

"You say them things cos you're upset," he said.

"No, I don't, Warren. I don't want some bastard doing over my flat, but I don't want you to think that I can't handle myself without a man's help—yours or anyone else's! I'm sick of it!" I said furiously.

My rejection stung him again.

"You bleedin' well need all those one-nighters up West with those poxy arseholes you meet at those godawful media parties and business bleedin' lunches? They really make you feel better? So what's wrong with me, George? Ain't I good enough? At least I think about you. Why can't you give a little to me and see?"

I lunged at him to slap his bitter face, but his arm snaked up and help my wrist.

"Me, I'm just the mug you call up for favours. You want to know? You want to know? I tell you, woman. I don' want to be no friend to you. Things have changed for me. I want more and I'm gonna get it, with or without you."

My wrist burned as his grip loosened. I was frightened. I stared at the person I thought I knew, and he was a cold stranger.

After a moment, he wiped his hand across his eyes and looked up at me.

"I'm sorry. I don't. . .can't seem to say the right things."

"Damn right!" I replied.

"I'm sorry, that's all. You better go to bed. I want to be by myself," he said.

I was hurt but I couldn't show it, I was too stubborn to do that.

CHAPTER SEVEN

I SLEPT RESTLESSLY BETWEEN WARREN'S white sheets, dreaming that I was running up a steep beach. A giant wave as high as a house, curled behind me, about to crash on to the shore. I ran harder to keep ahead, but my legs were tiring and I could hear the rush of the water curling over me, arching like a vast translucent cape. Then I saw the small figure of a man riding high in a distant part of the huge tunnel of water, but as he came towards me, I dived under to avoid the churning surf.

"George, it's eight o'clock," Warren said, placing a steaming mug of tea by the digital clock radio on the bedside table. He tapped the top of the clock. Details of the crash aftermath dominated the sudden loud news report. It was interspersed by commercials for security systems, carphones and couriers. Through slitted eyes, I glanced at the time and then at Warren. He looked very tired and I felt guilty for having stolen his bed and then having slept deeply enough to dream about waves and the sea.

We hardly spoke at breakfast. When I asked him, he told me he hadn't wanted to sleep, and had worked on the system for most of the night. It was warm in the kitchen. Rising from the table, he took off his sweatshirt, and rested it over the back of his chair, then he sat bare-chested opposite me. His shoulders were lean but muscled, little tight folds of even light-brown flesh ran down his stomach as he bent over the table.

"Look, I know you'll want to sleep this morning, but could you report last night's. . .business to the association's office. I don't know what happens now, you know, to all those things. . .my things. I want to junk the lot," I said nervously, when we'd finished our second cup. It was an imposition but I didn't have much choice, given the full day I had ahead, of me.

Warren nodded. "Where you gonna stay?" he asked, not looking up.

I bit my lip and held on to my pride. My silence made him raise his head and look at me. He leaned back and rummaged in his jeans' pocket, pulling out a set of keys. He placed them on the table and said, "It's yours."

"What do you mean?" I asked, confused and startled.

"This flat. It'll have to stay in my name, but just pay the rent. It's yours. I'm moving out today. Take the sweatshirt: it's cold out. That shirt and jacket won't be enough."

He got up and walked into the living-room, leaving me sitting like an abandoned mongrel, alone in the sunny kitchen.

"I'll leave you a machine and some gear so you can get your mail," he called out.

"But where are you going?" I said rising and standing anxiously in the doorway. His generosity and magnanimity were killing me.

He stood by his computer, with his maddening back to me, slotting a disk into its cover.

"I got another place, I told ya. Don't worry, I'll be in touch, and you can get me on the bulletin board."

"Are you being funny? Can't we talk about this. . ."

"No, babe. I just got to go."

I felt sick with disappointment. It was too abrupt an end and I didn't feel I deserved to be cast in the role of ungrateful cuckoo. There had to be an explanation for the strange way he had behaved these past days. He must have bought the new place already, assuming that I'd go with him, I thought, so my rejection must have been a real body blow. Disappointment and guilt turned to anger at his presumption – and then to pity. I hadn't asked him to change the rules of our relationship.

I turned, picked up Warren's sweatshirt, which smelled of smoke and herbal soap, and the keys. My jacket and handbag had been on the sofa, but when I looked over he was already holding them out to me. He seemed so frustratingly self-contained and self-assured.

I stood wretchedly in front of him and threw my jacket over my shoulders. With me in my high heels, our eyes were almost level. His hazel eyes were red-rimmed, and his mouth was set tight in a dark line above a clenched jaw. There had been precious few laughs between us this last week, but I remembered the good times and I knew there could be more. I wanted more. He had been my best friend –. I sometimes thought, my only friend – but there he stood cutting out, reducing, our friendship to the size of an electronic calling card.

I knew I felt something for him but it was not love, not as I understood it. If it *was* love, what kind was it? I wasn't sure I understood love anymore.

"What's going on, Warren?" I appealed to him one final time, trying not to cry and raising my hand to stroke his warm brown and shoulder. He tore my fingers from him, in what seemed to be exasperation, then turned abruptly away.

I made to go but he suddenly grasped my powerless hands, frantically kissing my palms, my wrists: dragging my face to his and sucking at my lips. His wild tongue pressed my mouth open and we staggered backwards towards the wall with the force of his unexpected caress. He crushed me against it and buried his beautiful face in my neck. There were no whispers, no moans, nothing that slowed or softened the physical dynamism in him. His arms pulled my weakening legs up, lifting me against his tense groin: and where we touched I felt the ache of response beginning to burn.

I dreaded losing control, and that was rapidly slipping away. I couldn't fight him, so I fought myself. I fought myself cold, and he sensed the ice in me. He stopped the onslaught, pumping his arms violently straight out so I could slip under them and away.

"I love you. I need you," he sighed bitterly, holding his head down, facing the wall, "I love you. Those other guys don't when they do it to you. It's important, so come with me. Please. It's no good here."

"Where do we go?" I said cruelly, watching the rivulets of perspiration run down his smooth caramel-coloured back, knowing now that he'd said what I had wanted him to say.

"Anywhere," he whispered.

The decision was mine. The dreamlike wave was upon me. What was happening to me and to him, I asked myself. When did he start to love me, and when had he started to fear and loathe this place? I has my own rules for emotional self-preservation and this man was asking me to jump.

"No," I said quickly, clearing my head.

He didn't look up, and I forced what was left of my own desire to sublimate into anger.

"No, you bastard. There's something wrong going on, with you, with me. I want to know what the hell it is, and I'm going to find out," I said, opening the front door and slamming it behind me.

It was a bright day in the city: the sort of fresh autumn day that sends fallen leaves and litter scuttling into heaps and swirls in the street, and spangled light glancing off red buses and car bonnets. I felt alive and strong. The sales team gave me a hard time about the length of my skirt, for which they received a one fingered salute, and I cheerfully explained my new homeless circumstances to Max. He was concerned, and I could see he thought my apparent good humour suspect. He wasn't to know I was high on rage.

"I have accommodation above the shop, as you know, Georgina. The guest room is yours for as long as you need it," he volunteered with unaccustomed generosity. "I have a housekeeper, of course," he added with an amused smile. "Our reputations will remain intact."

My confidence that day didn't stretch to badinage with the boss. As my hand pressed the keys I held in my jacket pocket, I recalled the nightmare I had left behind.

"Thank you, Max. I might have to take you up on that. I don't think I can go back to the block." I smiled appreciatively. Then I bit the bullet and asked for a sub.

He was mercifully understanding. After all, he remarked, a girl has to have a change of clothes. I wondered if he thought this line of playful teasing was making me feel better. I cheekily asked for time off to buy that change of clothes, but his equanimity wouldn't stretch that far and I went straight to my desk.

Celia Stevenson had already rung and left a message. I returned her call but she wasn't keen to discuss the information she had over the telephone, and so suggested a lunch meeting. Charlie mooched over for a chat. He had the weighty air of a condemned man. After giving him a few words of spiritual encouragement – the temporal would have dwelt on the benefits, if any, of bankruptcy – I patted his hand and sent him on his way.

The next thing I did was telephone Barnaby Page. His secretary took my call. I could almost hear him signalling frantically to her that he was not available.

"I am afraid he is not available, Ms Powers," she said.

"When *will* he be available, Amelia dear?," I enquired archly.

Her smooth Sloane voice hardened a touch. "Well, he's very busy, you understand."

"Can you give him a message then?"

The lovely Amelia's voice softened again, as she regained the upper hand.

"Why, of course, but I *have* given him all your others."

"Good. Now you can tell him to get right on the phone to me, otherwise he will find how incredibly embarrassing pesky little reporters can be with the help of a good contact book."

A few moments after I had replaced the receiver, it rang. I lifted it straight up. "Georgina Powers."

"Georgina!" breezed a familiar voice as if greeting a long-lost friend.

"Barnaby!" I breezed back.

"How can I help you?" he cooed.

"Lifestyle Software – I need all you've got."

"I knew it," he moaned. "I can't. I won't even talk about it. The whole thing's been a bloody nightmare, that's all."

Barnaby was very nervous. His voice had dropped to a whisper. "It's more than my life's worth, seriously, George."

"Barnaby, me old mate, your life, or more precisely your job, won't be worth a stamped-on semiconductor, unless you come across. I mean it."

There was silence at other end of the line as Barnaby weighed up the possibilities.

"Look, Georgina, I thought we were friends. If I tell you I'm seriously at risk . . ."

I cut him short. "We *are* friends, Barnaby. That's why I have to talk to you. I may be able to help you. Tonight at 7.00 pm at the Saigon. Be there."

"This is blackmail. It's . . .outrageous," he said angrily – but I got the impression by the time he put the telephone receiver down that we had a date.

I felt myself running out of steam. I had to keep pumped up. I had to keep myself going or I would lose my grip on this story, and on myself. Nick Weston walked into the office, caught my eye and waved an arm. I acknowledged him and looked away. Perhaps I was too harsh on Warren, I thought. Perhaps I should call him, perhaps he would stay and we could talk this through from the beginning. The urge to speak to him, to purge my regrets, was strong, but I didn't phone. I checked my mailbox all the same, and the bulletin board that we used. There was nothing.

I did a little more work on the stories Max had detailed, and left early for lunch with Celia. We met in a cosy Italian café near Old Burlington Street, frequented by smooth plump property men and art dealers. I chose it because it was safely off the manor. She was late. I had slid into the fixed bench quite easily, but when she arrived, she had difficulty squeezing in opposite me. She had put on a lot of weight.

Though I had prepared myself for this meeting time and again, nothing I had improvised was remotely relevant that day. We spoke easily, like old school friends who hadn't seen each other for years but could still pick up the threads of fond memories. She ordered a glass of wine and lasagne; I ordered Perrier and a mozzarella salad.

"Don't look at me," she giggled, "I know, I've put on weight. But you're so, so skinny, George. Fashionably androgynous, I have to say."

"Is that a compliment?" I asked.

"Why, yes! I'm jealous of course," she replied. I wasn't so sure, and I hoped she wasn't going to try and dominate this set-piece, now that she had relaxed.

In between mouthfuls, she sensed the increase in tension. Celia stopped and contemplated me. Her pudgy, ringless hands lifted a red napkin to her sauce-laden mouth and dabbed. Then she looked me in the eye.

"George, listen, don't mind me. I want to. . . help you, now. Look, let's get it out of the way. Eddie. . .I'm so, so sorry. I was so foolish, I can't tell you what a fool I was and how I wished and wished it never ever happened. . ."

"It doesn't matter anymore, Celia. If not you, then someone else. Forget about that now," I interrupted unable to bear the pain of her raising the emotional *Titanic* of my life.

She sighed and leaned sideways – with some effort – for her slim, black leather briefcase. She clicked it open on what was left of the bench beside her and passed me a slick plain-blue folder.

I pushed aside what remained of my salad and opened the folder. There was a single sheet of neatly typed paper inside. Underneath the title and corporate headquarters of Lifestyle Software, Inc. there was a list of directors. I recognised only two names, the major shareholders: Edward Charles Powers and Julian Kirren.The company had been backed by Kirren Ventures to the tune of three million dollars. I closed the folder quickly.

"Is this some kind of joke?" I asked coldly.

"Hey, don't shoot the messenger," Celia replied, shrugging her shoulders and holding up her hands. "Julian's dead; Eddie's alive. What happened to this little lot? The money, the loot, the lucre – and where did it come from?"

she said, tapping the folder. Celia was plainly enjoying this. She was enjoying making trouble for Eddie, I could see. I contemplated the depth of my own revenge and it was shallow by comparison.

"Can you use it?" She asked, sipping her wine with some satisfaction, and wrinkling her little fat nose. I knew what she meant.

"Far more than you could hope for, Celia dear," I replied, calling for the bill.

"Good," she said, patting my hand. "No, I'll pay. . .my treat. Let's keep in touch."

When she'd left, I ordered a chocolate-sprinkled cappuccino and pondered on the questions that the blue folder raised. My cousin had died horribly, murdered by a hypnotic message left for him in a computer, just as he was about to join a Californian software company for which he was apparently headhunted for a big fat fee. The software company had since wiped any tracks that led to it from Julian. Eddie claimed not to know much about the new job, and yet he was, and presumably still was, a director and major shareholder. If Julian was a shareholder and director along with Eddie, why was he headhunted, and, as Celia had noted, where did he get three million dollars for Kirren Ventures? By the time my coffee had grow cold and the chocolate had crusted, I had come to the conclusion that my soon-to-be ex-husband had reached the pinnacle of his long career in deception – and possibly a short career in murder. I had to bring him down.

Max was not best pleased, but I took a couple of hours off that afternoon to shower at a local pool, cut my hair, buy some new clothes and a pair of shoes. My feet were killing me. I told Max that another story had come up, and that it could be hot. I was buying myself more time. He told me to get on with it but to keep my eye on the ball: the City pages.

I waited for Barnaby in the gentle atmosphere of the Vietnamese restaurant until 7.30pm. Desperately tired and edgy, I had begun to curse him, when he hurried in and sat down testily. He stuck his head in the menu and muttered that was I trying to get him killed.

"Have you been followed or watched?" he murmured nervously. I'd never seen Barnaby sweat before, or even lightly ruffled, except by the the inevitable sartorial disarray brought on by a surfeit of drink. He had always affected an effete air of disdain – a result, no doubt, of the predictability and surefootedness of his own success. But life had blown him a raspberry. His top lip was bubbling with perspiration. Things were not turning out too well, and I could understand his confusion and resentment. He had my sympathy; after all he was an innocent entrepreneur in this nasty business, or so I hoped.

"Lifestyle. Tell me about it," I ordered, browsing through the appetisers.

"Nothing to do with me. It's a software house, I told you. It was set up to sell the programs I described to you. Look, I don't know how your cousin got involved. All know is that it was a straightforward headhunt, only they seemed dead set on him. I told you he wasn't the most qualified we put forward."

"Did you deal direct with California?"

"No, with the agent over here. . .Bloody bamboo chairs." Barnaby was whispering desperately, and in leaning forward had snagged his all-wool Savile Row jacket. It tugged him back and the poor man started as if the Grim Reaper had grasped his arm. A will-o'-the-wisp waitress now hovered, and I sent her quickly away with our order.

"I tried to drum up the business again, and I was told in no uncertain terms – and I mean in no uncertain terms – to go away and keep very very quiet. They threatened me physically, Georgina!" he protested.

"Who's they?"

"Him. The agent over here, Paul Danino – big bloody Yank. Probably one of the bloody Mafia. Jee – sus!"

Barnaby chewed on a comforting stalk of lemon grass, and I asked him to describe the man. The description he gave me – and Barnaby would have noticed a handsome man in some detail – could have been none other than my own husband, Eddie Powers.

"Do you know him?" Barnaby asked urgently, frustrated at my thoughtful silence, and wondering no doubt why I'd pulled out all the stops to get him there that night.

"I might do," I said finally. "Eat up."

"What do you know, Georgina?" he demanded, but I had no real answer for him. If I told him that the man who had threatened him so effectively had possibly killed his own best friend out of greed – and that he was my husband – the hapless Barnaby would have probably choked to death on his own froth.

"Not much," I said truthfully, "but, if I play this right, enough to draw their fire. The firm was backed to the tune of three million dollars by an unknown venture firm called Kirren Ventures. Remember Kirren – Julian Kirren? Your talentless programmer? Also a director and major shareholder. Your man Danino? I think he got rid of him for the three million dollars. You and your firm have been used as a cover, Barnaby dear."

"Holy shit!" was all Barnaby could offer before pushing his half-eaten plateful away and holding his head in his hands. Obviously he had come along half hoping for a rope ladder out of the situation in which he had found himself. Instead, he'd got firm advice to start digging.

"Let's go to the police!" he said, desperately.

I shook my head and poured us some hot rice wine from a china flask.

"Don't worry, Barnaby. I think I can distract this charmer enough so that he won't have time to bother with you, and anyway who's going to tell him we had this little meeting?"

Barnaby took a small cup and downed its contents. He looked about. We were alone but for two well-dressed young men – one European, one Japanese - three tables away by the window. Barnaby raised his eyebrows and rolled his eyes in their direction. His fashionable asymmetrical forelock bobbed up and down distraughtly.

I shrugged and popped the remains of a lettuce parcel of spicy beef in my mouth.

He couldn't wait for dessert or coffee, but tugged three ten-pound notes from a gold money-clip and tucked them under my plate.

"Untraceable cash is so much safer than credit in these circumstances, my dear. Keep the change and don't call me for a long, long time. I'm going away, taking a holiday. Don't expect a postcard. *Ciao*."

With that, Barnaby hurried out of the little restaurant and into the bustling Soho night. I finished the wine and ordered coffee.

Barnaby had filled in some important gaps, and I knew I had real problems, but the most immediate one was whether or not to return to Bow or to take Max up on his offer of accommodation. I couldn't face being alone that night; I just didn't feel that safe. Max's flat was close by; but if I went home, Warren might have been waiting. In my heart, I wanted him to be.

He could have been right: maybe I had overlooked him, taken him for granted, hadn't seen that he was offering more than friendship. He had been moving towards me through an emotional minefield, step by agonising step. Trying to jump the rest of the way had taken me by surprise.

The rice wine and the gentle oriental music reduced to maudlin regret the uplifting self-righteous anger that had sustained me all day. All that pent-up passion, too, going to waste tonight, I thought, laughing at us both and deciding that perhaps I could risk a little pride by going home.

I turned down Frith Street to make my way to the office so as pick up my clothes and call Warren one more time.

It was about nine o'clock and the street was less busy with people than it had been, though the traffic was still heavy. It was only when I'd stopped and turned back, remembering that I'd left my jacket over my chair in the restaurant, that I saw, walking briskly out of the restaurant, the two men who had been sitting by the window. The larger, bald European one carried my jacket in his hand, and now held it out to me.

Both wore expensive pinstriped suits, lightly striped hand-stitched shirts, and loud post-modernist silk ties. Their hair was cut short in business-like crops. They had encouraging smiles on their faces, rather like amiable, dead-eyed swamp crocodiles filmed grinning hugely and hungrily in wildlife documentaries. The European focused his hard blue eyes directly on me, and then he moved, too urgently towards me while his Japanese partner shifted around checking possible routes for my escape. I stood frozen in uncertainty as I felt fear. These were no concerned gentlemen returning my coat.

Turning quickly, I hurried urgently towards the offices of *Technology Week*, realising, as I weaved through the West End traffic, that I needed more time. They were so close behind me that if I had to stand tapping numbers into the security system by the door, I'd be caught. Old Compton Street was still relatively crowded with people and vehicles, so there was no chance of my diving for cover into a cab. To find one for hire, and moving, at this hour, in this traffic, would have been a miracle. I mingled with a crowd standing on the pavement outside a busy brasserie. Fear pumped up my circulation and flushed the rice wine from my sharpening senses. I tried to think, but I was beginning to panic.

The two hard-jawed men stood on the pavement opposite, waiting for me to break cover. A group of stylish young men in leather caps moved off from the crowd, north into Dean Street and I tagged along, pretending I knew them so that my pursuers might think twice before rushing in. The one in the group to whom I persisted in talking thought I was drunk. He put his arm around me and drew me to him, to gain the attention of the others. They ridiculed me good-naturedly, until one touched my behind and with feigned politeness asked the price of it. I kept up the act until it bored them, and they moved off. My followers then caught sight of me desperately isolated on the corner of the two streets and came after me.

It was a mistake, but I began to run down the almost empty street towards The Crown, banking on a crowd from the office being in there. The landlord knew me, too. I should have gone south towards Shaftesbury Avenue where the chance of getting a cab or at least away into crowded Chinatown was easier. I was moving further and further away from the sanctuary of the office, and Max.

I thought I was ahead but I could hear them panting after me, money jangling in their trouser pockets. Too soon, I heard the squeak of new leather shoes just behind me. Brutal hands grabbed my shoulders and waist and yanked me backwards. The smell of gentlemen's aftershave filled my nostrils as my captor twisted my head around and swore abusively in my ear.

"Nowhere to go, love?" the European said in a matter-of-fact London accent as he pulled me around and held down my arms. "No place to stay? Why don't you come with us? You might learn something about discretion and self-preservation." They hustled me across the street towards a narrow badly-lit side-road. I could just see a dark car waiting at the other end. Three gaudy women, two black and one white, stood smoking and talking together in a nightclub doorway.

There seemed no reason why not, and no better opportunity, so I started to scream loudly and frantically. As we lurched into the side-road, one man bent my arm up my back and the other grappled at my legs trying to lift them off the ground. Despite the pain in my arms and spine, I kicked out as hard I could, catching the Japanese on the chin. He swore, and slapped me hard in the mouth. My head swung painfully to one side with the force of his blow. With a basket-load of bad language, the women stepped out. The black women shrieked and cursed in remonstration, and the white woman – by far the largest of the three – grabbed the oriental's jacket and pulled him around, indignantly puffing up her not-inconsiderable chest. He shoved her roughly back with an obviously well-used insult.

This was his first and only mistake. Her pointed black-booted foot struck back at him, beautifully targeting his groin with a force that left him kneeling and moaning on the ground like a Moslem facing Mecca. Heavy handbags swung out at the stunned man still left upright, landing with the weight of well-packed suitcases on the back of his neck and the side of his head. His equilibrium truly shattered, he let me go and started to lope towards the car, holding up his arms to protect himself from the two black banshees who pursued him. Feeling increasingly isolated, his crippled Japanese friend staggered after him, clasping his painful crotch.

"Pansies!" the white woman screeched after them, before turning and tugging me off the ground. "All right, love? New on the manor?"

"Thanks – and no," I said, wiping my mouth on the sleeve of Warren's sweatshirt.

"You know 'em, girl?" one of the black women asked, smoothing her brilliant red blouse back into her red leather mini.

"No. The bastards just followed and grabbed me, I don't know why. But you were brilliant, and brave. Thanks so much," I said.

"City bastards. Come up here, think they can do what they like, take what they want. Good business, oh yeh, but they're snotty-nosed liberty-takers. Fancy taking a girl off the street!" The big white woman spat and started to make her way back to the doorway. "Go home now," she said to me, shooing me off.

With a wave of gratitude, I hurried down Dean Street towards busy Old Compton Street and the offices of *Technology Week*. There was nowhere else I could go. I had left the keys to Warren's flat in my jacket, which had been discarded in the chase. The whine and thump of games in the arcade opposite seemed to pick up my heartbeat as I punched my ID number at the door. There was the metallic taste of blood in my mouth and an ache in my jaw. My concentration on the door was so intense that I hardly noticed who was standing so close, until his hand clamped onto my shoulder and I leapt in fright.

"Jee-sus! you scared the life out of me! You OK? Did I

scare you?" said a familiar voice. My eyes were closed tight. I leaned on the door, hyperventilating, as Nick Weston stood in front of me, his steady arms held out to either side of me, in case I toppled one way or the other.

"Christ! What's happened to you?" he continued, obviously unnerved by the way I had jumped at his touch – and now aware of the swelling on my lip.

"Yes, you bloody effing, well did scare me. . .creeping up like that!" I spat at him. "I'm sorry, but I can't talk now. Is Max still working?" Still jittery and angry, but breathing more steadily, I pulled the door open.

"He was there five minutes ago. I'm sorry, but I saw you coming down the street. You look a bit shaken, so I'll come up with you."

"Do I really look this bad?" I said, horrified on catching sight of my dishevelled reflections in the mirrors that lined the reception area.

Nick nodded that I did. "Come home with me. I heard what happened at your place. Come home with me," he insisted. There wasn't much choice at that moment so I followed him out. I did not want Max to see me looking that way.

We walked down to Charing Cross Road and caught a cab to Islington, where Nick had third-floor apartment in a tall Georgian house next-door to a pub.It was tidier and cleaner than mine, spare and oriental, though not spartan like Warren's. The tasteful walls were hung with photographs, modern prints and paintings, and a set of stairs spiralled metallically from the living-room up into a huge converted attic bedroom which contained a freestanding claw-foot bath by a large fern-edged window at one end.

"What should have been the bathroom, I use as a darkroom," he explained as I looked around, then he laughed, adding, "but the toilet's still in there, so you'll have to watch yourself."

He started to prepare something to eat in his kitchen. I had already eaten and had no real appetite, so he offered me some red wine instead. I wanted to call Warren to see if he was still at home. If the telephone was engaged, he would be using his computer, and I could catch him later. If he answered, I could tell him what had happened and arrange to meet him.

Twice his telephone was engaged, but I persevered. There was a series of photographs arranged on the wall above the telephone. I presumed Nick had taken them. They were of a small child – she looked Eurasian – running down a grassy hill. He'd captured well the moment of childish energy and freedom. It made me feel nostalgic.

At last Warren picked up the receiver. "Yeh?"

"Warren, it's me. I'm so glad you're there."

"You OK? Where are you?" he asked, seeming concerned.

"At a friend's."

"Want me to come and get you?"

"No, no, it's OK. It's too late and I don't want to go out again," I said, dreading the thought of leaving this safe house. "I want to talk. We ought to talk."

"Listen, babe. . ." He sighed wearily, but before he could continue I blurted out in urgent whispers what had happened since I'd left that morning, including my theory that Eddie had planted the message that had killed Julian. Warren did not comment on any of it. Instead he repeated his offer to come and get me.

"You're playing a dangerous game, babe. I know you – you want dig the dirt on your cousin, and get Eddie, but you want the story for that bleedin' paper, too, doncha? It's only a job. Be cool. You could be getting yourself killed. I'm gonna leave, I told ya. Come with me. Let's sort things. There's still time. We'll be OK anyplace."

The frustration and desperation in his voice failed to move me as much as his analysis of my motives. It was disconcertingly accurate. He had put his finger right on my pulse, and he was mostly right. I'd stirred up this cauldron for a news story and for revenge. The question was, which way did the scales tip?

Nick walked into the room carrying a plate of pungent stir-fry and the rest of the bottle of wine, and I brought the phone conversation to an end.

"I've got to go now, Warren. I'll be in touch, I promise," I said hurriedly.

"Maybe. I know you're with a man tonight. You trust him? You want him?" he whispered in a broken voice.

"He helped me off the street, Warren. I was in bad trouble. Anyway, since when do I answer to you? Before we talk about this again, sort yourself out. You're missing the point, you're missing everything," I whispered angrily.

"No, not me – you. *You* are," he said harshly, cutting me off.

Nick was politely ignoring our exchange and expertly scooping his dinner into his mouth with chopsticks. I sat down morosely opposite him in a wide soft armchair.

He topped up my glass.

"Don't let the. . ." he began, as he pushed his empty plate away.

". . .bastards grind you down," I finished and smiled ruefully.

"You got it," he replied, pointing a playful finger at me.

He was very thoughtful. He asked if I was warm enough and did I want a bath. To the first question I said I was, and to the second I remarked that my personal hygiene seemed uppermost in people's minds nowadays. He remained serene at my display of irritation.

"I just thought you might like to wash the street from your face and feet," he answered gently. I looked down at my muddied shoes and held my hands out. They were grimy with dirt and blood. Suddenly, I felt lonely, hurt and cold, and it must have showed.

"OK. Hot bath, right now. I'll get you a towel and you can wear my dressing-gown," he ordered, jumping up and running upstairs.

"No peeking," I said trudging upstairs when he eventually called me.

He had pulled down a creamy-coloured Roman blind over the window and had filled the bath with hot water and a herbal foam. Rich-coloured rugs from the Far and Near East were scattered around the bath and across the pale-stained floorboards to the double futon at the far end

94

of the vast room. It was covered with a violet coverlet screen-printed not with any Eastern motif, as I would have expected, but with a line drawing of Rodin's "*The Kiss*."

It was a room that did not proclaim wealth but a certain sensuous style, a comfortable place to lie and, presumably, to love. I looked around, wondering where one kept the soap in the Court of King Yuppy. It was in a black marble bowl atop a leggy table by my side.

When I'd finished bathing and I trotted down the stairs, Nick looked up and beckoned me over to sit opposite him again. He had prepared me a glass of hot whisky and honey, which I refused, protesting that it was a tipple I found rather disgusting, especially, when a malt and water was an alternative option. But he insisted, and I accepted the glass with excessively gracious thanks, and sipped slowly from it.

We didn't speak. He was waiting but I wasn't going to discuss my traumatic day. He rubbed at the dark stubble on his chin.

"Do you want to go to sleep now? Have my bed. I'll sleep down here," he said.

I told him I wasn't ready for bed; I was still buzzing. He got up and walked over to his ample record collection that lined two shelves of a wall.

"Any preferences?" he called over his broad shoulder.

"Nothing too loud," I ventured, and he pulled out one or two alternatives, then changed his mind. He stood there for a while reading a variety of sleeves, until he smiled at one and placed it carefully on the turntable.

CHAPTER EIGHT

THE TINKLE OF COTTON CLUB jazz splashed out of the speakers, and Nick turned smiling towards me.

"Bit bluesy, not too sad," he said, sitting down and dragging a packet of cigarettes towards him across the table. "Smoke?" he said, offering the packet to me.

"No," I replied.

"Mind if I do?" he said, throwing a cigarette up adroitly and catching it between his well-shaped lips. His thumb flicked at a cheap, throwaway lighter which bore the logo "Fix". He lit his cigarette and inhaled deeply.

"Greek beer," he said, pointing to the logo.

"Are you Greek?" I enquired.

"Half. My mother," he replied. He got up and patted the pockets of his loose grey cotton drill trousers. "I think I've got some grass somewhere. It's not bad. Want some?"

"No thanks," I said, feeling surprisingly inebriated. By way of conversation, I voiced my admiration for the pictures of the little girl.

"My daughter," he replied, taking a picture from the wall, coming back and sitting down. "She's got a new daddy now."

I mumbled an apology but he just shrugged, and took a fragment of tobacco from his tongue. He had a gap between his front teeth, and the smoke from his exhalation seemed to steam out of it. The acrid smell billowed over the table. He took a couple more deep drags and stubbed out the cigarette impatiently.

"Got to give up," he said, leaning back and spreading his solid arms to either side of his sofa before tucking them comfortably behind his head.

The late evening passed by in virtual silence but for the music. It was not that we had nothing to say. The jazz and the rosy red wine had lulled us into a kind of quiet, restful, thoughtless inactivity. Eventually, I got up a little unsteadily and allowed him to escort me upstairs. I sat on the firm futon with its arty bedcover and waited for him to leave.

"Can I take some pictures of you?" he asked as he stood by the stairs.

Time to be cautious, I thought.

"I'm too drunk. Anyway, what about the lip?"

"The bruise isn't too bad. It's on one side of your face. Anyway, I don't want to take pictures of your face," he said, crossing his thick arms.

"Do me a favour," I replied world-wearily, tugging his dressing-gown up over my neck.

"I'm a professional photographer. I'm not going to rape you. You've got good skin and I like your body. It's angular and tough, like a boy's, a street kid's. You'd be an interesting subject."

I closed my eyes and lay back on the bed, my bare legs dangling over the edge. Had I had a day of it. First, my best friend contorts himself into an incomprehensible ardent suitor. Second, I discover my cousin is involved in a monstrous fiddle and my husband probably murdered him for gain. Third, two sharply dressed thugs try to abduct me in the street. Fourth, the safe house turns out to be run by a well-built, possibly homosexual, porn peddler.

"You mean object, surely?" I said sarcastically. "Thanks, but no thanks. It would spoil our fine working relationship. By the way, have you come out of the broom closet yet?"

Nick walked over to the bed and looked down on me. I looked back, my defiance blurred by the minor quantity of liquor I had consumed. He started to laugh. Warm laughter that came up from his belly and shook his shoulders. I rose up on my elbows, and he sat next to me on the bed and patted my leg.

"First, I am not gay. My remark was a professional comment, that's all. You do have a boy's body. Second, my photographs appear in leading quality publications all over the world. I always work for Max because he's an old mate. Third, I have had my nudes exhibited at most major galleries. We are not talking centrefolds here. We like to call it art."

A lesser person might have felt sheepish at this point, but I wasn't about to be cajoled into artistic union with a pompous Greek with a swollen head, whose idea of a global career move would be an major exhibition of my private parts.

"I have my mother to think of." I leant back again, crossing my arms over my face. The fact that he was a friend of Max was awe-inspiring. I gave Warren a cursory thought, too. He would certainly take a dim view of such photographs – a very dim view. At this silly little private joke, I began to laugh; and the more I laughed, the sillier it seemed, and so it went on. Exhausted with mirth, I spread out my arms and Nick sat there, smiling.

"Good," he said, when my laughter subsided. "I'm glad you're not angry. But I'd still like to photograph you. No funny business. In your own time. . ."

"Just art," I smiled wryly, rolling over on my side.

"Just art," he said, and got up to go.

I watched him walk to the stairs, his long dark hair curling past the collar of his large blue checked shirt. He was very likable, I thought: refreshingly direct and undemanding. I'd always picked men with a dark side. They seemed to interest me more. Unfortunately, the very intrigue that had originally attracted me was inevitably turned against me in the end. I fell for men who had to cheat.

I lay musing for a while, and then I got up and walked slowly down the stairs.

"I want you to make love to me," I said, slurring just a little.

He had a coffee on the side, and was choosing another album. He placed it on the turntable, and the sound of an undulating saxophone filled the softly lit room. It was a sound like the taste of dark chocolate sundaes.

"Sonny Rollins," I said.

"Right," Nick replied, raising an eyebrow at my correct assumption.

"Did you hear what I said?" I asked.

He took his coffee over to his deep blue sofa and sat down.

"Yup. I thought I did. It was a little unexpected. You won't let me take a pictures of your body, but you want to have me lie on it. Strange," he said, looking steadily at me.

I shrugged nonchalantly. "I thought you might be refreshingly different."

"Ah. . .so you choose your men like you choose your cocktails, do you? Let's have one with this funny name, this cute shape, this super colour; a splash of this would be nice, would be refreshingly different. . .Very flattering, very sexist, very sad – very Georgina Powers. Well, you *have* got a bad case of hope triumphing over experience there, my dear. I'm a big bad man with a cherry on top, just like all the rest. . ." he replied, putting his hand inside his shirt and rubbing his hairy chest.

I didn't turn to go. He looked pretty good, sitting there like an avuncular satyr smiling mockingly, his big brown eyes laughing at me.

" . . . and I do have a girlfriend, I'd like to be faithful to," he intoned, like a newscaster adding gravitas.

I said goodnight politely, walked with dignity up the stairs, and lay naked under the golden and violet layers of his bed.

I closed my eyes and was almost asleep when his feet padded across the floorboards, and I heard him say, "On the other hand. . ."

We made love three times that night, and once in and out of the bath. The first time he lasted a melting minute in my lazy embrace. The second and third, he spent hopping on and off me and massaging my flesh. It was a testament to his staying power, athleticism, yoga classes – and my good nature. Nevertheless, I was reasonably content as, in the quiet shadows of the early morning, I lay with my arms around his thick-set waist while he stroked me.

"Come with me," he said eventually, taking me gently

by the hand. We walked naked to his white Victorian bath.

"Not again," I giggled. "I'm really clean, honest."

When it was over, he carried me – my arms loosely entwined around his neck – to his bed. I looked into the curls of his long, coarse hair as I rested my head on his broad shoulder. The trouble with orgasms is that you become unreasonably attached to whoever you're with when you have them. My King of the Fairies, or Bottom – how could I know? One thing was certain: I didn't really care. I was back from the dead.

We slept past the alarm. There was no time to share breakfast or ask how it was for each other, because another press day at *Technology Week* had come around.

Nick prepared his case and then rummaged in a cupboard. He drew out a red crash-helmet.

"We'd better go in on my bike," he said, digging out an old motorcycle jacket for me to wear, too.

"The return of Locust Woman," I said when I was dressed and we were ready to go.

"You look fine . . . well, on second thoughts, you look weird!" He laughed, pushing me towards the door. I would have hit him but I couldn't find my arms.

It didn't take long to weave through the traffic to work. At first, I held tightly on to Nick's waist, but my body soon fell in with the rhythm of the machine and I rested my hands casually on my knees. Every now and then, Nick let go a gloved hand and stroked my leg. Leaning against his cold, hard leathers, it felt like being in another city, one I could actually see. My usual route to work entailed worming my way in on the tube, squeezed into an airless underground carriage, pressed up against a stranger I didn't like the feel or smell of. People who talked, but weren't talking to me; other people's news pushed into my face. Eye contact generally avoided: stare and look away, stare and look away. Travelling without a ticket is an offence. Travel with one can be offensive.

100

That day the cold morning chill of the city was cutting my cheek. I could look around and see people, dogs, parks, houses, and traffic in one perspective, stare up at the soaring masonry of huge metropolitan buildings, see the ice-blue, cloud-scudded sky and the remnants of a morning star.

We were exposed. There was danger all around; at every side-road, crossroads, roundabout and traffic-light cars and pedestrians came at us. The jerking acceleration of the bike, and Nick's steel-toed riding boot, kept us ahead. A raised gauntlet, a tipped visor brought us into the network of other bikers making the run. Here the city was in perpetual motion and we were in it, seeing it, smelling it. The complicated cogs were cranking away, working some way or another. Cause and effect, that's the system; and it's a system that works.

We arrived on time, and only Max raised his pale, bearded face to look up when we entered. Everyone else was head down and hard at it. We grabbed coffees and I went straight to my desk, while Nick sauntered over to Max. Tomorrow was settlement day and I had to tie up a few loose ends about the back-office machines, and how the brokers' technology would be coping. Lifestyle would have to wait, for the moment. Charlie East wasn't in, as yet, but Mary Stow came over to check a few story lines. She kept staring at my face, and I lifted my hand to my cheek. I had forgotten about my bruises.

"Perks of the job," I said, touching the tenderest spot near my lip, and trying to laugh. "We ought to get danger money."

She didn't laugh much, and I couldn't blame her. Whatever the cause, it was obvious to her that it had not been an accident. She must have been only a couple of years younger than me, but she looked as if she had just left school: bright, keen, intelligent and naively enthusiastic. I could have been envious of her, but I wasn't – I couldn't bear to do all my learning again. Under her immature, concerned gaze, the more unpleasant aspects of the evening came back to me. I could hardly believe that two hired thugs tried to kidnap me. It couldn't have been random choice; they had spent the evening in the restaurant while I talked with Barnaby, and then they had followed me.

Barnaby! I'd forgotten about poor terrified Barnaby. I rang his number straight away. He was not in the offices and Amelia told me frostily that Mr Page had taken an extended holiday. I prayed that no one had got to him before he'd a chance to pack his elegant little case and leave.

Unless they had been watching Barnaby instead, the two heavies must have seen me leave the office. It had to be Eddie's doing. He had threatened Barnaby, and now he had threatened me. Clearly he was the behind the break-in at Julian's, and had left the knife in my flat. He had been warning me, just like Warren had said. I was sure now. Warren had been right to be nervous; he'd read the signs, but he hadn't known it was Eddie. With the help of the information dear Celia had deposited with me, I could get back at him. But I had to get to the root of Lifestyle, the point at which three million dollars entered Kirren Ventures – and perhaps poor, dead Julian would have to help me.

My telephone rang – it was Nick. He wanted me to meet him in the studio and look at the photographs he had taken at Broadwick's, before the art editor made a choice. They were to accompany my possible front-page story and the inside feature.

Max watched me as I walked out of the main office and into the adjoining studio. Perhaps he was genuinely concerned, or perhaps just curious. I didn't usually care for such niceties, but this time I hoped Nick had been discreet.

He was leaning over a light-box when I pushed open the door of the busy studio. I perched on a table behind him and waited.

"Right," he said finally. "I've weeded out the dross. See what you think."

"What did you tell Max?" I asked, hating myself.

"That you had obviously been assaulted, and you didn't want him to see you in such a mess, so I took you to my place. You didn't tell me what happened, so what could I tell him? He's a bit concerned about your run of bad luck."

"OK," I said sheepishly, relieved he had misunderstood me.

The pictures were as good as I had expected them to be, given Nick's frank resumé of his own success and reputation. He'd captured the atmosphere of the "crash". The paper-strewn dealing room of wall-to-wall screens seemed as windblown as an air-traffic control room with the windows open. There were extreme close-ups of screens, red with falling money, reflecting the dealers' grey faces peering at them. A couple of prints superimposed the wall clocks timed to the world markets on to the regular blocks of processors in the computer room.

The shots of Kay Fisher were superb. He'd caught her attitude, the dominatrix disguised in a powder-blue suit, somewhere between nanny who knows best and the snow queen. There was a tense one of her standing beside the unlucky, desperate-eyed Des Pritchard, with her vast super-successful dealing room in the background. There was also one of her sitting on her desk, with crowds of screens and dealers behind her, as pretty as a porcelain figurine transported into an arcade game. She was the perfect misfit, the one who was in control.

I chose that one, and earmarked an unusual selection showing her hand moving away from the screens. Nick had taken them as she sat with her back to them. There was a blur of white movement where her hand had lifted away for a fraction from the columns of red figures signifying the crashing market. Nick had obviously been fascinated by those pale delicate fingers with such a surprising grip on the City.

"Good," he said, marking them. "I'm going to blow up this last set. Gary'll choose them, too, if he's got any sense." Gary Macintyre was the art editor, a suave, deceptively easygoing "ideas" man with heels chronically calloused with digging in. I was surprised at Nick's optimism which was, as it turned out, ill-founded. Gary subsequently chose the ones with the dealers' grey faces against the red screens, and the tense one of tight-arsed Fisher with poor old Des.

"The guy's a dickhead. Those were OK, but definitely not the best," Nick whispered, as he later stood by my desk. He wasn't angry, just irritated and surprised. I was trying to write and he was distracting me. His physical presence in my peripheral vision was tantalising. I wanted to touch him.

"Be with you in a minute," I said, biting on a well-chewed pencil. It was 3.00pm, and Max and the subs would be waiting. Gary was a pussycat by comparison. He stood silently by as I added the final touches to my piece and sent the copy into the network. My egg muffin and fries lay cold and congealed in their ozone-eating carton.

"Let's eat," I said, dropping my unwanted lunch over the back of my desk into my wastepaper bin.

"Let's talk," he replied.

Before we left, I called Warren. His telephone was engaged so I left a message for him on the bulletin board. It said that since his keys had gone with my jacket, which was God knows where, I felt safer at Max's for the time being. I wanted to meet him urgently the next day.

As Nick and I relaxed, drinking cappuccinos and eating Italian buns in a crowded local patisserie, he broached the subject of my bruises and how I'd got them.

"Some yobs tried to beat me up, that's all," I said, knowing that if I told one piece of the story I would have to tell him the whole thing. "Happens to us girls all the time."

He looked down at his cup. There was an uncomfortable silence that I needed to break, so I asked to see his photographs again: the ones of Kay Fisher's hand dragging away from a screenful of red numbers. I studied them one at a time. There was an ethereal quality to the moving hand, and in the blur it created, which appeared to pull numbers in its wake.

"Probably a bit too arty-farty for the paper. Can't you sell them somewhere else?" I said.

Nick looked annoyed. "'Course."

"I like them. I do. I do," I added.

"Never mind that," he said. "Are you OK, for tonight?"

Subtlety was not his strong point, I thought, amused – until he added that Max had told him that his offer was still open. Max had told me, too, via a neat little green message on my screen.

It was like a kick in the guts, but I should have expected it. Nick had a girlfriend he'd have liked to be faithful to.

"It's cool," I said with scarcely a flicker of emotion, unable to meet his eye, and staring hard at the photographs.

"Is it?" he asked.

"Yes, sure," I said, pretending to be endlessly fascinated by the share prices.

He said, "Good," and so did I.

"I had a nice time," he added.

"Yes, it was nice, wasn't it. Let's do it again sometime – when you're next in the area. I'll try to be sober."

There was nothing more to be said. It was another one-night stand that I had invited. That's how I like it. It just happened to have turned out to be pleasanter than most. Nick was a nice, mature guy and we could still be friends. These thoughts queued up in a standard orderly fashion, forming a lifeline that would rescue me from the ache of emotion in my chest. But I was fooling myself: I was bitterly disappointed.

Warren was right. What did I get out of these guys, and why didn't he – a real friend who loved me – count? I felt ashamed. For Warren, for myself. Nick wasn't refreshingly different at all. He was a big bad man like all the rest, like he'd said. A man, like all my men, who had to cheat. This time, I'd helped him cheat someone else.

He opened his hand for the photographs and, as I handed them to him, I noticed something in the upper middle of the screen in the photograph I laid on top. Peering so closely before, I hadn't noticed the pattern. I had thought at first that it was a minor flaw which had arisen in the initial development process. Then I noticed that the irregularities together formed a faint word superimposed on the list of information comprising the FT 100 index.

I flicked through the photographs. It appeared on three others.

"Have you got the contact strip for these?" I asked briskly, all the mush of mixed emotions pulped out by the fresh anomaly bristling in my mind. Nick said that he had and I asked if he could blow them *all* up for me. He noted the urgency in my voice and agreed.

"But why?" he asked with untypical curiosity.

"Because there is a word showing up on one of the screens – yet it's not in all the pictures. It's a bit strange, given the state of the market."

"Why?"

"It says BUY."

CHAPTER NINE

THE WARNING LIGHTS HAD CLICKED on in my brain. I hadn't noticed a message of this size on any screen when I had visited Broadwick's. The message might have been part of the real information displayed for the market makers and dealers, of course. A flag, for all to see, which would warn them to change tack. It might even be a routine procedure, now that the City had computerised. If so, it would be easy to check.

I couldn't make myself believe that. Buy or sell *what?* would be the first question asked. The world was selling, so what organisation could be advising its people to buy so indiscriminately? I had never heard of any firm that offered such a service. Most relied on analysts' reports on particular stocks, shares and sectors. These highly-paid financial oracles stood up above the crowd of heads and screens, fast-talking their advice into microphones when times were really hectic. In any case, Des hadn't mentioned that his system could analyse information as it came in, and then automatically push out its conclusions on to the screens. I would have picked that up.

It was suspect, and I couldn't help making the connection between it and what I had seen on Julian's PC.

Nick studied the same photograph while I shuffled through the rest. They revealed nothing.

"Could be," he said, ordering more coffee and a fluffy, unrequested, cream cake for me. "There's definitely something there. Could be a word. Could be a *trompe l'oeil.*"

"Good Lord! Well I'll be. . .one of those? Not a development flaw, perchance?" I suggested wryly, pushing the calories aside and wondering why I wanted a cigarette so badly.

"No, not a development flaw. Be nice, Georgina."

We sat in silence. Waiting patiently for an explanation, Nick smoked his potent cigarette while I tried to assess whether I could trust him. I wasn't sure. I thought I liked him, but I wanted to be so cruel to him now, to poke needles under his warm, hairy skin. He'd made me feel so good, but where was the meaning in it? There was no meaning. It was transitory. Tense, nervous, headache? Take a muscular upmarket photographer every three to four hours. Works like a dream. It was a dream. I really should have been more objective and gracious about it all – made it easier on him. Poor man, what did he know?

It was so hard to know. How do you know if it's a good, or a bad thing making you feel good or bad? Experience – you must have *first-hand* experience. Vicarious experience isn't so risky, and you don't get to feel the pain. You don't have any of the real fun either. Brave talk. There I was, experiencing learning from experience, and it was crucifying me.

There was, undoubtedly, room for doubt. It occurred to me that Nick had been conveniently close by on the night that I had been almost abducted. He had wanted to take pictures of my naked body. A photographer of his calibre must have had pulchritudinous women aplenty, queueing right up his spiral stairs. So why did he want a bruised bag-of-bones like me? Could it be that he had a more practical reason than art, or lust even? There was more than one way to skin a cat. More than one way to threaten someone, to make someone stop. Eddie would think of something underhand like that. Did Nick know Eddie? I had to be more careful, I thought. He was staring at me and I stared back trying to decide.

However I cut it, it came out square: Nick just didn't fit the role of villain. His eyes were too well set and clear. His eyebrows moved consistently with the rest of his face. Even his ears had a fresh honesty about them. He might be a little disappointing in his follow-up, but he was straightforward. I could forgive him a lot for being so attractive, too – like a waiter in a holiday romance might be, sweetly diverting but not dangerous. Celia would like him; she'd say he was yummy, a sweet thing. He didn't wear too much aftershave either. Not like Eddie.

No, Nick said what he thought, even about himself. His photographs were good, and he said so. He told me he was like all the rest. And he didn't want to carry on. No lies, not yet. My finger circled the edge of the cake-bearing plate.

"How did you take this snap?" I asked, finally, taking the photograph from him and studying it again.

"Do you mean to be insulting?" he said, biting on the end of a spent matchstick. I looked up and smiled sweetly. Smoke drifted from the ashtray and his stubby cigarette across the moist wooden table towards me. I didn't avoid it, I wanted to taste its smell.

"Of course. And if I am complimentary, it is quite by accident." He laughed and rattled off the technical details.

"Tripod. Camera – Hasselbad. Lens – standard 80 mm. Film-Ektachrome 64, so it would handle the artificial light, $2\frac{1}{4}$in by $2\frac{1}{4}$in, so I could get a decent-sized print from the slide. Bracketed the f8 meter reading by four stops either way so I could over and under expose and get at least one photo with the blur right, shutter speed $\frac{1}{60}$th of a second . . ."

"If a message came up on the computer screen every, say, sixteenth of a second, or twentieth of a second, would you catch it?"

"And get it clear? Pretty hit and miss. Logically, at a sixteenth of a second, I'd have a one-in-four or one-in-three chance at that shutter speed, but getting it clear as well, a one-in-forty, one-in-thirty chance . . ."

I nodded and held up my hand to stop him.

"How else would you get something that is not supposed to be in a picture on to it?"

"You mean overlaying the word on to the image of the screen? Double exposure. Of course, you can get double images in a studio by using projectors."

"And did you?"

"No."

We looked impassively at each other. He was silently challenging me to continue. The patisserie was busy, packed with the Soho café crowd. The air was sticky and close with the smell of sugary confections and the smoky aroma of steaming coffee, chocolate and burning tobacco. The silence between us lay like a still, infrangible block within the chatter all around.

I picked a packet of brown sugar from the bowl near his ashtray and crunched it satisfyingly between my trembling fingers. Why were they trembling? Was it the lack of sleep or the buzz of caffeine that was making me jumpy? Or nervousness – "the instinct of self-preservation"? I remembered reading that in Roget's Thesaurus at school, before a big exam. The instinct of self-preservation. Knowing hadn't helped. My body was steeling itself for some unknown threat coming from some unknown direction. I was beginning to feel sick: perhaps it was hunger.

"Can I keep this?" I said, holding up the photograph.

"Sure."

I thanked him and slid it carefully into my bag, before pulling the now irresistible cake back towards me and nibbling at it. I told him that I wouldn't need any blow-ups – what he had said was enough. He didn't ask me for the explanation I surely owed him, and he didn't get it.

A message that shouldn't have been in a pizza-house computer had meant death; but this message, if it was what I thought, had been insinuated into one of the biggest and most complex financial systems in the world. That meant a killing of a different kind. Either I had stumbled across it by chance, or someone was trying to tell me something.

Nick's dark eyes moved away – a reprieve. He'd seen someone he knew: a tall blonde with a glossy red mouth and no buttocks. He rose to speak to her, and I hurriedly took the opportunity to slide from my chair and leave while it was still light.

"Georgina, wait. . . I want to help you," he called, but too late. I was already out of the door, caught up in the woolly hats, saffron robes and jingle bells of a passing chanting Krishna troop. One with a beatific smile and a creamy stripe down his frozen nose thrust an advertisement for a vegetarian restaurant into my hands. Zen and the art

110

of manna marketing. I sighed. Everyone was at it: chasing that pound note, that dollar, that yen, that camel through a needle's eye.

I waited for them to jangle past me, then tried to cross the busy street – too late to catch the whining sound of a motorbike changing gear. It accelerated and swerved, missing me, but only just. My foot slipped as I tried to avoid what had already gone, and stumbled over the kerb. Someone took my arm and I clutched my bag, afraid.

"Bleedin' machines. Could have killed you. Ought to put a stop to them, I say. Still, 'e's making a livin' I suppose. All right, love, steady now."

An old Londoner with wayward eyebrows and a gummy smile had grasped my elbow. With his old flat hat and brown, leather-elbowed, tweedy jacket, he looked like street-corner news vendor. His smile faded at my fixed expression of fear.

"All right, luv? 'Ere, you all right?"

I stood up with difficulty and smiled vaguely, thanking him all the while. The old fellow laughed with relief and, patting my back, stepped smartly on his bow-legged way. I looked back at the coffee shop, full of bright young things in black. Nick was nowhere to be seen.

Back at the office, Celia had left a message for me to call, and so had Anne.

Celia told me something which I had half expected, that Kirren Ventures was registered in the Cayman Islands and was ostensibly a venture capital company established to manage Kirren Ventures Capital: a fund of investment money raised through syndicates of professional investors. The fund totalled just five million pounds to date, three million dollars of which had passed to Lifestyle Software, Inc. No doubt it had reserves in a nice discreet hole-in-the-wall in Zurich – a tried and tested haven for shy investors.

"Who runs it, Celia?" I asked.

"Who do you think? Edward Charles Powers, Julian Kirren and a someone listed as K. Fisher. There are other names, some Japanese. It stinks, sweetie, it stinks. How did you get on?"

This was part of the hidden agenda: she gave a little, and then I gave a little. This way our friendship was being rebuilt on tiny vengeful favours. I told her about the fake deal with Hitec; how Eddie had played the part of Lifestyle's US agent and had recruited Julian. She got very excited.

"The bastard! He's getting a lot of money, from somewhere. I suppose when Julian died, he wanted to stop anyone tracing Lifestyle back to Kirren Ventures. Bit of a boob calling it that, though, don't you think? Of course, he must be holding on to Julian's share of the money. I'd like to know what they did to get it."

It was getting increasingly difficult to think clearly. I was trying to handle three emotions: a throttling excitement at the magnitude of the story I had in my grasp; a skin-prickling horror at its implications, personal and private; and the plain fact that I still quite liked Celia. It was hard to control my voice under these circumstances.

I couldn't tell her what I had discovered in the photograph. I couldn't tell her how a software program had killed Julian and, what was more, was possibly manipulating every dealer in town at that moment. So I said nothing, and she rushed in like Mother Nature filling a vacuum.

"Do tell! do tell! . . ." she pleaded.

". . . There's a call on another line. Sorry, Celia, I must go . . and, oh, thanks, thanks a lot. I'll be in touch."

"Do. Do. Come round for supper or something. We must talk."

I made a mental note to talk to my solicitor about Celia's role in my divorce, then looking up I caught sight of Charlie's lugubrious form shuffling away from his desk.

I called out to him to come over.

"What's the city been doing since Tuesday?" I asked.

"Market dropped like a stone until today – then there was a fairly strong rally. Not enough to make a difference to me." He shrugged miserably and made to turn away, unaware that he was giving me the result of the message in the photograph.

"I'm really sorry. Listen, can you hang around for a bit? I've got some calls to make now, but I need you to go over something with me."

He shrugged again and nodded unenthusiastically, before retreating to get us some coffee.

Meanwhile, I called Des Pritchard at Broadwick & Klein, under the pretext of a follow-up to my feature.

Des was more than a little offhand until I asked if, in an urgent situation, the market-makers, brokers and dealers received guidance on what to buy or sell – apart from the analysts' reports, verbal and written. He wasn't sure what I meant, so I asked, more directly, whether his computers analysed the flow of information from the Stock Exchange, Reuters and so forth, and then delivered automatic "buy/sell" advice to the screens in front of the dealers. Still confused, Des began to speak, thus buying himself time in which to understand my question.

"I hear what you say. The thing is, how long is a piece of string, Georgina?"

"I don't know, Des. How long is it?"

"Well, let me put it simply for you. We put an enormous variety of messages on our screens. . . . We're talking messages on screens, right?"

"Right. A direct message thrown up onscreen which says buy or sell."

"Yes, good, well. . .at present we are not set up to 'massage' the information which we receive from the great variety of databases, external and in-house, and deliver it in that very specific way to the desktop. However, it is something we are looking into. With the great strides being made in the field of artificial intelligence and expert systems, there are programs which exist and which we could utilise to create our own analytical expert system, which the inhouse customer – and by that I mean, of course, the market-makers, brokers, and dealers. . they are the customers of this management information services department, after all – which they could use as a decision support system, non-interactively or possibly interactively. We are continually looking into new ways of satisfying the demands made upon us, you understand."

He meant "no", but I played along and asked some cheesy questions about "state-of-the-art" expert systems and whether analysts would eventually be replaced.

"You just can't computerise a gut-feel, Georgina," he concluded with some satisfaction, after at least twenty minutes of vacuous deliberation.

Oh, can't you? I thought and, thanking him for his help, slowly replaced the receiver. He had confirmed, albeit verbosely, that the message had not come from any official source in Broadwick & Klein. Nick's camera had indeed captured an illicit intrusion into a supposedly secure computer system. I hoped the photograph was genuine, and I still couldn't think of a good reason why Nick would have faked it. It didn't matter that he didn't want me; I wanted him to be one of the good guys. I had to be right about somebody.

I knew I was right about who was manipulating the market. It was Eddie. My darling, darling, fast Eddie and possibly his woman, the alabastrine Kay Fisher. If they were handling the Kirren Ventures account, in which they had an interest, that was a clear breach of US and UK dealing rules. Kay Fisher was the chief of trading of the London subsidiary of a major US securities house, and Eddie was a broker-dealer there. It had the makings of a major international scandal. Celia's information had provided me with a story which, on its own, would make headlines in every newspaper in every major financial centre of the world. But I had to sit on it: it wasn't the whole story – not yet.

Technology Week's office machinery began to orchestrate its early-evening cacophony of paper shuffling. It was amazing that anyone could get used to that cranking factory noise. I hardly noticed it most days, but that evening it made my weary head ache. Max had his ginger head down, analysing and checking and, curiously, his glinting hair made me feel a little wistful. Nick's hair was long, thick

114

and dark. It smelled of cigarettes and soap. It took a couple of dreamy seconds before I mentally kicked my own arse.

To hell with him – this story was going to make or break me. Where was my perspective, my sense of proportion? I had stumbled on the tip of a City scandal, a computer scandal and a murder, all three of which certainly involved my aberrant husband, and he was out there looking for me because he knew I was on to this – somehow he knew. I looked at my dead computer screen with fresh suspicion and foreboding. Did he have a message for me? Could he really be thinking of killing me?

I logged on, and left a note on the bulletin board for Warren to meet me that night at a certain bar, if he could, if he would; and, if not, at least to get back to me. I had to nail Eddie's foot firmly to the floor. I had him on one level, thanks to Celia, but for the rest, a photograph alone couldn't prove anything. I had a plan, but Warren would have to help me make it work.

A yellow gummed notelet on my screen reminded me to call Anne. As I tried to connect, Charlie pulled up a chair and sat beside me with two coffee cups. I shooed him away again. The poor man wandered off, embarrassed, like a modern-day Captain Oates searching for a tent flap.

Anne insisted on bringing me up to date with the family news, chiding me in her sweet county voice for not ringing my parents. She had managed to contact Richard, my cousin and, now, Anne's only brother. He wanted us all to get together again.

Richard was a newly qualified doctor on Voluntary Service Overseas somewhere in the Sudan. His arrival brought back uncomfortable memories of the last time we had all met, at Christmas, when he inched the conversation away from the rise of property prices in the South East to describe the appalling Sudanese practice of female circumcision. As the women shifted their positions and began to chew their knuckles, his father blustered that it was hardly an appropriate topic for after-dinner conversation, and a row had ensued about what might be. Personally, I was so affected that I wouldn't let anyone near me for weeks.

Nevertheless, we fixed a date for a filial gathering, and Anne finished detailing the more trivial events of her week. She'd brought a new dress for a dinner-and-dance. Her mother was having trouble with her ovaries. She mentioned, in passing, that Julian had received some mail, mostly dubious catalogue stuff, and she was desperate to get his name off whatever free mailing list these companies shared. I gave her an address. Then she asked if I had I heard of DP Projects Ltd. I had – it was a large recruitment firm supplying contract programmers to customers who need short-term computer staff.

"Why?" I asked guardedly.

"Well, Julian has been sent a cheque from them for £105.69. It relates to an underpayment for some work he did back in July."

That seemed unlikely, given that Julian had worked for Pull-Up For Pizza for years.

"Does it it give any more detail: dates or place?" I asked.

"Oh, yes, here at the bottom. . . 11th to 16th and 18th to 23rd at the Research and Development Department, Information Services Division, the Stock Exchange . . ."

"Shit." I muttered to myself.

"Pardon?"

"Sorry, spilt coffee. . . Poor Julian, must have needed extra money for him to have done outside work on his holidays from the pizza house."

"Oh," she said, a little unsure.

Anne then became a little tearful. She said how ironic it was that he'd secured that well-paid Californian job so soon after, and now he was dead. I said it was, and tried to comfort her. My duplicity depressed me.

Then, catching me off guard, she asked me about the break-in. It had been preying on her mind.

"It was Eddie," I admitted, preparing to spare her the whole truth.

"But why?"

"I think Eddie was trying to hide something from us. He knew about Julian's job all along. He was a reference or something. Perhaps Julian had written something about

116

one of Eddie's schemes on his disks. Or perhaps the new company didn't want to be linked with such a. . . let's face it . . . such an embarrassing misadventure. It's Eddie's way of doing things, isn't it? Sneakily."

"But why not just ask us?"

"Why not, indeed?"

I'd omitted the worst, but Anne was, by her standards, 'very, very, cross' and threatened to ring Eddie 'to give him a piece of her mind and find out what his little game was'. I suggested otherwise, pulling a bit of a stroke – as Warren would have called it – in the process.

"Think of me. I can't stand any more unpleasantness, not now, not with my divorce and all. . ." I pleaded, shamefully. "Let me handle Eddie, please. I'll be in touch. Promise."

I replaced the receiver and dragged my hand across my mouth, wiping beads of perspiration from my upper lip. I couldn't believe how things were panning out. Julian had esconced himself at the Stock Exchange just long enough, presumably, to set up his invisible but not insignificant little program, a mysterious little spanner in the works of the Stock Exchange's grand computer network. All he had to do was hide the code in the innumerable lines of code that existed, and instruct the thing to send the message out at under one sixteenth of a second. No one would notice, not the computer managers nor the financial community, following the strange urge they got to buy and sell. It was all quite painless for the victims. So far, only one person, my cousin, had been terminally hurt. Poor Julian must have stepped way out of line.

"Charlie!" I stood up and waved to him across the office. He waded through the wasteland of cartons, cups and crumpled paper towards me.

"You all right?" he asked, pointing to my face. I kept forgetting about the bruises, but people *would* keep reminding me.

"Yeh, yeh. . . Sit down. Look, I know this is perhaps not what you think yourself best qualified to talk about at this moment, but I want you to tell me how to make real money in the City."

He groaned, placed an imaginary pistol to his head, and pulled down his thumb.

"Bang," he said. "Big bloody Bang."

What he told me made it sound all so complex. But it was simple really; especially if you knew what was going to happen next, and if you knew that the game to be in was index options and futures.

CHAPTER TEN

I HAD TO TELL WARREN. He hadn't left a message for me, so I swallowed my pride and called his flat on the off chance he might still be there. The line was engaged, which meant he was still around, at least. I stuck another message on the board and spent the time while waiting for him to call by browsing in the paper's library for information on the Stock Exchange's computer systems. Charlie didn't stay long; he hadn't wanted to go down to the pub with the rest of the team. He was so low that he went straight home to Earls Court, stone cold sober. Poor Charlie, he had definitely started to worry me.

Max and the subs were now checking the page proofs. The night before publication day was reserved for last-minute stuff, the front page, and late-breaking stories. The inside pages had gone through much earlier in the week. At about 8.30, Max called me out of the library. He was alone.

"I was quite pleased with your work this week, Georgina," he said, as I stood by his desk. "Of course, I felt it lacked a certain. . .shall we say, concentration. But" – and he looked up at me with his level, unmatched eyes – "all's well considering, um. . . isn't it?"

I wasn't sure that he meant, or what to say, so I said nothing, but stood uncomfortably by his desk, waiting for the verbal uppercut which would surely follow. Max liked to play games like that. He was like a satiated ginger tom pawing a trapped mouse for entertainment rather than its edibility, reminding the hapless rodent that, even in forced, neutered domesticity, there was still a hunter at home.

"How's your jaw?"

"It's OK, thanks."

There was a pause. Max turned away, ostensibly to look

something up in a thick directory. He tapped at his keyboard.

"I presume you're working on Lifestyle. So what have you got?"

I was shocked to hear him mention it. Lifestyle had become so personal to me that I had forgotten anyone else had an interest in it. I wasn't sure what to tell him, or how much I wanted to. The telephone interrupted us. Max picked it up, balancing it between chin and shoulder so that he could casually flick through the directory again.

"It's for you . . . Warren Graham," he said, moving his eyebrows up. I nodded and he indicated to me to go to my desk. I waited for the click of the replaced receiver before I spoke.

"Hi, thanks for getting back to me."

"It's OK."

"You're still at the flat then?"

"Nah, I'm somewhere else now. I can still check the board."

This conversation was taking some time to crank up. It was as if we were talking with satellite delay. His voice was glum, listless and mechanical. He seemed indifferent to me. I reckoned it was no more than I deserved, but I began to think our talking might be a pointless exercise, that I could no longer count on Warren as a partner in my jolly computer capers.

"You all right? What happened to you?" he said, showing some concern at last.

"I'm OK. I was a bit shaken up last night, I'm sorry, but I couldn't talk there and I can't really talk here. This Lifestyle thing is an even bigger scam than we imagined, Warren. You just won't believe what I have to tell you."

"'Cept that you're in more trouble, yeh?"

Warren was so stuffy sometimes – so neat, clean, safe, and so bloody patronising.

"Look, I am taking your advice. I'm being careful. Honest. C'mon, Warren, this is the biggest, biggest, story . . .

can you meet me tonight? I've got something you'd like to do."

"Doubt it."

"Oh, c'mon, man, do me a favour. . .please?"

He agreed reluctantly, to meet me sometime after 9.30 in a pub we both knew, close to the office.

I put the receiver down and walked back to Max.

"Where were we?" he asked, knowing full well.

"Lifestyle."

I don't know why but, heart pounding, I pulled up a chair and told him just about everything – The Untouchables version. I left out the sex and drugs, and a few names, to protect the almost innocent and hide the almost guilty. I told him about my lunch with Barnaby, about Julian's strange demise, the missing disks, the message in the computer, the fact that someone wanted all links between the company and Julian wiped out, the list of directors – but without naming Eddie, or Kirren Ventures. Then I told him about my flat, the two men in the street, Nick's photograph of the Broadwick screen, and Julian's holiday job at the Stock Exchange. I didn't mention Warren.

"Get me a coffee," he said when I had finished and he had paused to absorb the gush of information poured out for him. When I returned with a chipped mug for each of us, he was puffing on a thin cigar. I hoped he'd offer me one; I was desperate for a smoke.

"Great. I can see it now: 'SEX-MAD BOFFIN MURDERED. CITY BRAINWASHED.' The tabloids'll have a field day."

My face must have registered the frustration I felt, and Max held up a pale hand to prevent me jumping to any further conclusions about what he thought about my story.

"If – that's if – you pin it down with facts – you'll have a quality story for this paper, and the nationals can do what the hell they like. Proof? You haven't got any real proof or any real crime. A few dubious connections, that's it."

"Well, my source at Hitec won't say anything – I don't expect him to – but the Lifestyle connection is recorded. We know how Julian died and we could retrieve the

121

message, with or without the help of the pizza house. We can prove that certain items disappeared from his cottage."

Cigar smoke shot upwards from Max's cynical mouth and he began to think out loud. "You say there's a murder and a fraud, a type of insider dealing only worse, bigger – manipulation of the whole market. The Stock Exchange would be most interested, the Securities and Investment Board, of course, and the DTI. If there's a US connection, the Securities and Exchange Commission would really kick some ass. Can we connect the two stories?"

"I have a lead that connects them."

He paused to inhale again and then slowly released a cloud of blue-brown smoke, this time from the side of his mouth. It was a fascinating technique, but watching it made my concentration drift.

"Your cousin? How do you feel about that?" he said at last.

"OK."

He'd made the wrong assumption and asked the wrong question. Never make assumptions in an interview, or you miss something for the sake of a lucky guess. Who? What? Where? When? How? – that was the stuff. He hadn't asked, so I didn't have to tell him that it was my husband I wanted to hook and land, struggling and gasping on my stony shore. But if Max had broken a basic rule, then so had I. A journalist's job, the manual says, is to observe and record life, not get involved in it.

"OK, so we have a message on-screen that kills a computer programmer: your cousin. That is difficult to accept in itself. We must get a record of that, and some evidence that such a form of hypnosis can work. I presume it does, otherwise why would its use in advertising be banned? Now, this programmer worked on programs for the Stock Exchange computer systems. You are assuming that he implemented a message, similar to that which killed him, on to that Stock Exchange system. We need a record of that, and not just a photograph. You are also suggesting that he made enough money doing it to set himself up in business on the West Coast. Why? He should have made enough to retire on."

"I think Julian really wanted the business, and the money was a means to that. He is – was – not a real crook. He was killed for that money, and for some sort of indiscretion, I'm sure. He put his money into the business. It was respectable. He didn't have to explain to anyone where the money came from, since he was ostensibly an employee headhunted by the firm."

"And a major shareholder."

"Yes, and if he had wanted to, he could've said that his shareholding was valued in terms of his professional contribution: that is, the main product of the company – those so-called lifestyle programs. I think he needed to hide behind it."

Max stretched to one side and flicked a long length of ash into his ashtray.

"Problem one: who else is involved? Problem two: what is the scam exactly? Problem three: how do you prove it so that we can print it?"

The story was as hard to pin down as three bars of soap in a communal bath. *I* knew who else was involved and, having talked to Charlie, I knew – and thought I understood – how the money was probably being made, though not in fine detail. Providing it was another matter altogether.

I'd found out from the library that the SEAQ computers monitor their own activity to a certain extent, and are continuously monitored by other computers. The transactions aren't automatically recorded, but all the on-line quotes and trades are, by a separate set of computers. Those run programs which shadow the activity in the market and make sure that all the market makers are playing by the International Stock Exchange rules. Market makers are the wholesalers, who buy and sell shares and they use SEAQ – the Stock Exchanged Automated Quotes system – to register deals of how many shares they are prepared to trade in and at what price. They purchase and sell stock

123

to any number of people but they can also buy and sell on their own account.

Market makers replaced the jobbers who used to stand around under chalkboards on the Stock Exchange floor, notebooks in hand, taking orders. The boards displayed the shares they dealt with and the prices they offered and accepted. Jobbers couldn't deal on their own account, and it was their word that was their bond. Nowadays, the market maker's word is as vulnerable as an electronic blip.

When market activity moved from the floor to desk tops all over the City, the Exchange had to ensure that the same information on prices and trades was available to everyone at the same time, just as it had been in the past. It had to ensure that market makers played fair in pricing and in registering their trades. Unfortunately, new technology had eroded old trust.

There is now a Markets Supervision section which monitors trading activity and its computerised on-line market surveillance system of screens and ticker feeds will flag any misdemeanours. Erratic behaviour such as: excessive spreads in a quote, jumps in price when trades are executed, late trades, is duly noted and questioned.

Trading activity in the various US stock exchanges is similarly monitored by computers, which take note of unusual movements in price or volume and reconstruct the pattern of trading in any stock that could be involved in a violation of the market rules.

The main securities regulatory authority in the US is the Securities and Exchange Commission, more ferocious and dourly bureaucratic than the insipid, and laissez-faire, UK Securities and Investment Board. Both have access to electronic files which could link stock exchange members' firms with possible insider dealers among their clients. They have the power to peek at the firm's books – turn up uannounced and audit the financial and computer systems of the firm.

There was no automatic execution of trades yet in the UK.

At the time of the crash, deals in London were still being confirmed over the telephone and once negotiated they were, hopefully, registered with firms' own computer systems. Some deals were being scribbled down on little pieces of paper, which is why there was going to be so much rummaging through pockets, delving in drawers and discreet kicking out of sight of wastepaper bins on settlement day. In such a blizzard of transactions, who would be sure who said what to whom and when and, more to the point, who recorded it accurately.

In spite of all this white noise of information, I was sure that an audit trail of Fisher's and Eddie's activites would be slithering through the system somewhere. The SEAQ computers monitored other movements through the system, but again I wasn't sure of the detail. Most computers with any pretense at security have an activity journal: a sub-program which checks what is happening while the computer is switched on. It could be a diary which simply records when someone logged on and logged off, or listed what files and programs were used, and when.

Truly paranoic systems record every tap on a keyboard. Paranoia, however, has its price. The more the computer's electronic watchdog has to guard, the greedier for computer time and space it gets. The bigger the police state, the less freedom for the people, in this case, the less computer resources for the users for whom the system was actually built.

I guessed that the SEAQ computers had a threat-monitoring system which would record any unusual computer activity. The fact that the authorities hadn't picked anything up yet – and I couldn't know for sure whether they had or hadn't – meant that Julian's program was being accepted as a normal function of the system. If he had been involved in part of the development and implementation of certain Stock Exchange programs, he must have ensured that when his program was activated, no alarm bells rang. Even so the computer's diary would have a note of when Eddie or whoever logged on to change that message. Perhaps no one had noticed, perhaps no one ever checked.

The grand scale and purpose of the Stock Exchange system, a huge network of computers handling and disgorging

125

an enormous amount of information, added to the difficulty.

SEAQ comprises three large minicomputers which accept information from one hundred and twenty market makers in UK securities, equities and gilts. Another three minicomputers absorb information from forty-five international dealers. The computers share information and note company announcements and information on traded options. The EPIC database, which calculates a range of stock indices, is run by three more computers.

The bid and offer dealing prices, the size and time of the quotes of over four thousand securities are amassed and delivered to a further twelve minicomputers which form the SEAQ TOPIC information distribution system. They feed a variety of specialised Stock Exchange information services, and those of outsiders such as the Reuters news agency, to the City.

The information gathered is sent in pre-formatted pages over the telephone network to City desks. A TOPIC screen might show prices of UK equities and gilts or international securities traded in London; prices from other international markets; company announcements, dealing prices on the London traded options market, private information from market makers and financial specialists for selected clients, the LIFFE financial futures prices and FOREX foreign exchange service live from major banks. There is even a computer-to-computer link so TOPIC can be blended with securities firms' own in-house computer information.

In London alone, there were at least thirty-two interlinked central computers in two separate buildings of the Stock Exchange. These were connected via leased lines to over two hundred computers in offices of member firms and service companies. More importantly, the TOPIC information distribution system displayed SEAQ data via specially-designed terminals and personal computers on more than ten thousand cluttered City desks. Every second of every day, someone somewhere was gazing at a TOPIC screen.

126

The surveillance teams had enough to do making sure the market makers and broker-dealers were behaving themselves in the maelstrom. When the big crash came and prices were sucked down at speed, they must have been working at full stretch. In fact, TOPIC computers were unable to handle the changing prices quickly enough to keep pace with the market. There was a record volume of trading activity, an estimated seventy-five thousand per day as opposed to a more usual thirty to fifty thousand. EPIC had been running twenty minutes late and eventually the link between EPIC and TOPIC collapsed and the service displaying the indexes and changes in stock prices was temporarily suspended. Dealers rushed to use the telephones to contact the market makers, some of whom were conveniently out to lunch.

The newspapers were full of stories of dealers crying foul and accusing the market makers of flouting the rules by not registering their trades straight away, even trying to cut losses by not trading at all. On the floor of the exchange there was nowhere to hide but the gentlemen's lavatories. With new technology, you can duck behind the telephone. You simply let it ring.

The computers had also been caught out by the small rally Charlie had described that day, the one, which to my mind, coincided with that BUY message Nick had photographed. Prices had surged 50 points. The surveillance team would have had enough to do shadowing that fireball without checking out a program no one could see.

No one would be looking out for a tiny parasitical program which was piggy-backing its way to every financial dealer in the city and possibly the world.

Happy Birthday Eddie, I thought. Happy Birthday to you. You smart bastard.

He knew exactly which way the markets were going to move, because he was in the driving seat. And Charlie had given me some ideas as to the potential for using that truly sublime extra edge.

Though he had experienced trouble with the practical, Charlie's financial theory was sound. From what I could comprehend, the financial games worth playing were *futures* and *options*; and if you wanted to speculate on markets as a whole, futures and options on stock-market indices were favourite because each point on an index is valued in *cash*. It was a punt; and there wasn't any question of investment in real stocks and shares, which, individually, could perform at odds with the overall market.

Traders in the conventional option markets merely buy and sell a *right* to buy and sell the underlying index or stock at an agreed price a few months hence. Certain pre-packaged options are *traded* – bought and sold over and over again as their life decays – on the options markets of the world: Chicago, New York, Philadelphia, London, Amsterdam, Paris, Hong Kong, Singapore, Tokyo, Sydney and Bermuda.

Charlie had been patient in his explanations, but I had a real problem with the jargon as much as with the concepts at the time – but then I have a problem grasping the technique of getting favourable rates of exchange when I go abroad. I always think that understanding some things is like holding butter: the firmer you think you're holding it, the quicker it turns into something else.

Charlie spoke of *writing puts* and *calls* and *buying puts* and *calls*, of *spreads* and *straddles, strips, strangles, bells* and *whistles*. He wrote things down and did little sums for me, which helped, but for all his patience I didn't reward him by telling him why I wanted to know; and he, like the good fellow hack that he was, didn't ask.

Charlie explained that "*put*" options – conventional and traded – are geared to a *fall* in the market, and "*call*" options to a *rise* in the market, depending on whether you are buying or "writing". Just as in much of computer journalism, in financial circles writing meant *selling*.

"In the US they trade the S&P 100 – a point gain or rise in that index is worth one hundred dollars. In the UK, the Footsie is the hottest option. A gain or loss in that index is worth £10 a point. The buyers can trade their options in the indices at any time during the life of the option," Charlie explained. "So, you see, an option has its own value which can be traded, and it is a function of a number of things: the time left ticking away until its expiry or exercise date, the difference between the striking price and the current price of the underlying index, dealing costs, and the volatility of the market."

He started to warm to his subject and told me, with a bitter half smile, that he had heard that some put options – bets on a fall in the index – had increased in value one thousand times during the week of the crash.

I made a metal note of that while Charlie lapsed into a deep, quiet depression. I poked him in the ribs and he began again.

"'Course, for every buyer there has to be seller. Buying puts and calls are only half the story, that's the game for us lot. The other half is the professional half – what the traders do, that is, *selling* or *writing* of these options. The writer of a traded option gets paid the premium – and takes on its liability. A trader who writes *call* options expects the market to *steady* or *fall*, because he has to supply cash or sell shares to a holder of a call option should they decide to exercise that option and buy. A trader writing puts expects the market to rise. Remember, it's all about buying when prices are low and selling when they are high. You mustn't get caught promising to deliver at a higher price when prices start to collapse.

My eyes were glazing over and my mental faculties were turning to fudge, but Charlie waded on.

"Some traders 'write naked'. Writing naked is the same as selling stock short, that is, selling stock you don't own and hoping you can buy it cheaper later in order to deliver it. Naked writers make bundles of money from small price movements – if they get it right. The liability, of course, is unlimited."

"Look, Mum, no safety net," I suggested.

"Right."

"The truth now – did you dabble around exposed. . .naked?" I inquired.

"You bet, but I was relatively lucky losing only £50,000, a mate of mine lost a million quid."

129

"A million! What? Shit! Was he a trader?"

"No, he's still a bricklayer."

"So what was he doing up there with the man from the Pru? What's more, what were you doing there?"

"Just walked into my local bank, they put me through to securities, and we were in business. It was a raging bull market; no one thought they could lose. But we were all wrong, weren't we?" He gave an unhappy sigh.

"Christ! The trouble I had getting an overdraft. . ." I muttered.

Charlie smiled ruefully and looked glumly at his watch.

"Look, sorry, but I want to get out of here. . . you know." He raised his heavy eyebrows towards Max.

This game obviously had the capacity to generate as many ulcers as profits. With a small calculator and the inside track, it would be such easy money – lots and lots of easy money. It would have been easy money for Charlie if the bull market had kept on going. But it didn't; someone had made sure of that. Someone had decided it was time to play bear.

Options weren't the only possibility. There were other systems which could be worked for gain. Eddie and Fisher could have played the forward and futures markets in foreign exchange if they knew the dollar was going to dive.

If stock prices go up, so does the value of a futures contract; if it goes down, the contract holder makes up the losses. Traders who think the prices will go up, buy stock index futures hoping to sell them at a profit. Traders who think they will go down sell stock index futures hoping to buy them again at a lower price. Eddie and Fisher must have sold their contracts months ago.

Before the crash, futures and options trading was so intense that billions of dollars worth of futures were being traded on the Chicago Mercantile Exchange, outstripping the value of actual shares traded on the New York Stock Exchange itself.

In all of this, and particularly in the US where the stocks, futures and options markets are separated, computers are

130

used to calculate when to move, and how, in and between those markets.

This so-called "program trading" in the futures market and stock index arbritrage is largely confined to the US and to US securities houses. Program trading used to describe the use of computers to calculate the outcome of buying and selling large blocks or portfolios of stock. Now it's used to describe almost anything that involves a trade and a computer.

A handful of US investment houses dominate the game of stock index arbritrage. Their computers monitor futures and options in Chicago Mercantile Exchange and their underlying stocks and shares in New York. On the day a futures contract matures, the computers, which take into account all the costs of trading and dividends to be earned, too, crank into action to calculate whether the two prices on the two exchanges are diverse enought to buy on one market and sell on another for a profit.

This technique needs automatic matching and execution of trades by computer, too. In the US this is done mainly through the small order system of the New York Stock Exchange, NASDAQ, a system designed to handle small orders of one thousand shares or less. The computers take charge and choose the best price without fear or reason. When the turmoil in the market was at its height, the New York Stock Exchange had to order a halt to this system, fearing it was forcing the market further downwards.

Another form of program trading also linked to US futures and stock markets is portfolio insurance. It's a way that pension funds and big holders of stock like to hedge their bets and literally insure their portfolios, just as people insure property – though I don't or rather couldn't, in the case of my flat in a high-risk tenement in Bow.

Big investors do not necessarily want to sell their stocks and shares for short-term gains, or even to avoid losses in a falling market. Selling their shares in a falling market would depress the market even further, and reduce the values of the shares they hold. Instead, by dividing the portfolio into stocks and safe government gilts or bonds, they spend their time shifting between the two types of investments. Instead of selling shares when the market is falling, the pension funds sell futures. By selling a stock index future when the market is up, they know they have already made their money if the market and the index subsequently fall. If they have sold, and the index goes up, they only lose the premium on the futures contract – a fraction of the value of each underlying stock whose actual value goes up. Smiles all round and computers make sure the balance is right: that the investors hold shares when the market is rising, and sell futures when it is falling.

Things went wrong during the crash. Once unleashed, the bears in Chicago expected the stock prices to keep falling, and stock index futures plummeted much further and faster than the stock-market did. Instead of the usual one-to-two point difference between the stock and futures index, there was a yawning gap of twenty, twenty-five even thirty points. Instead of a few per cent of the portfolio, the cost of the futures insurance premium on the portfolio was costing half as much as the expected losses on the shares. At least when the price of corn falls more than five cents a bushel in one day, trading stops. There was no such white flag in stock index futures.

The London market had crashed even more severely than that of New York, even though the scope for computer-assisted arbritrage and portfolio insurance was limited. The vertical slide couldn't be explained away by computers and the futures markets. The City had no such program or small order trading or automatic execution of trades by computer. The futures market was on nothing like the scale of Chicago either, but London still saw a huge difference between index futures and cash prices displayed on the SEAQ screens. There were no program trading systems to blame in the City. Something else was driving the market.

Kirren Ventures, Kay Fisher, Eddie Powers, and possibly Broadwick & Klein of course, had been using one or all of these markets to screw the rest for the tidiest, most profitable turn. I knew how they'd pushed the market in London, but I had yet to find out what tipped it on Wall Street. On thing was sure, they'd used a rogue computer program; and, ironically, honourable computer programs were being blamed for their crime.

The photograph, or rather the negatives, proved that something extra was on that screen: something that could move minds, and so move markets. What we couldn't prove in black and white was who put it there and who had exploited it. So far, I could only link Fisher and Eddie to Kirren Ventures. The SEC and SIB didn't like brokers or dealers with undeclared interests in customer accounts. It would make headlines as a malpractice scandal, particularly when we found out how big a client Kirren Ventures had latterly become. But this story was more than malpractice; it was manipulation on a grand Machiavellian scale – and it was also murder.

Max was right: I needed proof. I had to catch them red-handed to prove continuity in the crime. I had to link them to the message, to the program, and to the system.

"I do have a plan which won't set the hares running in SEAQ security," I said tentatively.

"I thought so," Max replied.

"Someone has to be altering the message."

"Of course."

"So someone has to have access. From the information I have, I'm presuming that it's not someone in the Stock Exchange's computer division, but an outsider. I know someone who can check the voice and data communication lines going in and out and find out what's going through them. The stock exchange computers are linked to customer sites by leased lines. My own theory is that someone is getting round them by actually dialling into the central computers with a PC when they want to change the message. There are ways to dial-in; engineers and demonstration computers have that facility so it's not impossible that someone has commandeered one. We find it, tap the line and tape what's happening. We could even hijack it and demonstrate how it works."

"A little electronic eavesdropping? I understand, but you won't be able to check the whole City."

"No, I told you I have a lead. It's at Broadwick & Klein."

Max raised a golden eyebrow. This meant he was impressed – I think. It was always hard to be certain with Max. While I contemplated his inscrutability, he contemplated whether to give me the go-ahead.

"OK," he said at last. "Get on with it and record everything, and I mean everything: conversations, the lot. Meanwhile, I'll get Mary Stow to do some foot-slogging around the City and see if anyone has noticed the market going against expectations. Even if everyone is being brainwashed by this little program, *someone* has to be checking why they got it wrong."

"Why Mary? What about Charlie?"

"Charlie just might be on the way out if what I've heard is true. I hope you don't know what I mean, Georgina. . . or at least, come Armageddon, you have something significant to bargain with, something that I want such as an unbeatable, award-winning front-page story."

He smiled slyly at me. There was the squeeze, a little pressure from his spikey paw. If I had even needed any more motivation, he'd given me just that little bit extra. Get the story or lose your job – and he meant it. He was a hard man. My cheeks flared up with a warm guilty glow. I bit my lip and nodded before mumbling my excuses, and leaving him.

As I picked up my bag from my desk, he called me over again. This time there were no props, no cigar, no directory, no tap-tap-tap on his keyboard. He leaned back in his chair, with his pale, blue-veined hands on the armrests, and looked directly at me.

"I expect you to check back here tonight. If you don't turn up, or haven't rung in by 1.00am, I'm calling the police. My housekeeper already has a bed made up for you, if you don't have another place to stay. I don't want

134

you to take any personal risks whatsoever. A smack on the jaw is one thing, but it could easily turn out much, much worse if the perpetrators of this think you are on to them. Off you go now."

So off I went – to find Warren and enlist his valuable, if reluctant support.

CHAPTER ELEVEN

I WAS LATE BUT WARREN was waiting by the bar of the crowded pub. He'd created a space for himself by a pillar and was watching the door. The liquid sound of early Billie Holliday danced up from a basement club, into the smokey bar above.

Warren had seen me enter, and watched unsmiling as I pushed my way towards him. The hint of shock in his face and the occasional stare from one or two drinkers reminded me of my roughened appearance. I hadn't seen myself in a mirror for a while. The jaw ache had almost gone, but I kept forgetting about those maturing bruises on my face.

Warren looked different, too. He was dressed to kill. In a smart suit and shorn of his dreads, he looked sharp, serious and businesslike.

"Who did that? New boy?" he asked wryly, handing me a glass of honey-coloured wine.

I rapidly picked open his cigarette pack as he paid for the drinks, peeling two crisp notes from a gold money-clip.

"Two rather aggressive young men in City clothes, actually. Nick – that's his name – is not the new boy; he's the paper's freelance photographer, a friend of Max's, and he kindly took me home. I was in a state, I tried to tell you, but you were too pig-headed to listen."

I felt that the corroborative detail helped me lie more convincingly. The cigarette hung from my lips unlit.

Warren obliged without comment, and as his cool hands cupped a flame to my face, I noticed his stiff shirt cuffs, new and white against his smooth café-au-lait skin, and the glint of a gold watch on his wrist. On closer inspection, I could see that his dark grey double-breasted suit was hand-stitched. His deep green silk tie lay on his shirt as flat and cold as a pike.

"Wick-ed but what for? Interview or something?" I mocked, fingering the lapel of his jacket.

He took my hand gently, but firmly, away.

"I'm going somewhere later."

He was polite but distant. I wondered if it was with a woman, and whether I would see her. I was tempted to ask but I didn't dare needle him any more. Warren had lost his sense of humour somewhere along the way. I'd lost mine, too. To someone as recently rejected as I had been, there is something particularly galling about seeing a latter-day suitor dressed up to the nines for someone else. I secretly wanted him to look as wasted as I was. Instead, he presented an open disregard for what common decency lays down as an acceptable period of angst.

With some irritation, I asked for some roasted nuts and a bag of crisps, which he duly ordered and paid for while I looked about for a discreet corner where we could talk. If I had been early, or even reasonably on time, there might have been space. Instead, I had to move closer to him, pressing in on unwelcoming, resistant territory. The tension between us was strung out like an electric fence.

I stood awkwardly munching the crisps, self-consciously crunching in his ear between sentences, aware of their vinegary smell, and of licking the salt from my fingers. I would never have been bothered by such a thing before. He would probably have fought with me to empty the bag. Our childlike friendship had splintered like broken glass.

I decided to tell him my story anyway. I didn't drink much, but I felt high and light-headed. I grew more animated and excited as I spoke, dragging incompetently on a cigarette whenever I paused for breath. Warren listened impassively as I related what I had found out about the message, and as I tried to explain how I thought the market had been manipulated, and why. I continued speaking through his silence, breathing in his smooth, musky aftershave, smelling my own vinegary breath. His hazel eyes glistened, glassy with lack of interest, like marbles in sand.

Finally, a little unnerved but grinning triumphantly, I

137

told him what I wanted him to do. It was my trump card. If that didn't get to him, nothing would. But I was doomed to disappointment. He was unenthusiastic.

"You on pills?" he asked dourly, taking a swallow of his gin.

"No!" I replied, indignant and cross. I had little right to be offended, given what he'd previously seen me throw down my throat, and – I hate to admit – throw up. But this time the accusation was unjust. I was wild-eyed, yes, but I'd had damn all sleep and very little to eat. Warren's flat cold response to my brilliant story was infuriating.

"You mean, get the old BT overalls on and tap the lines?" He wasn't looking at me.

"Sure. All you have to do is walk into the switching room at Broadwick's where all the voice and data lines end up, bug the data, and pick up the noise. Record everything. It's got to be there. Look, Julian set the program up to run when SEAQ runs, OK? The message goes out on the same leased lines that all other information goes out on, OK? But Eddie has to be able to change it – so there must be a way in to let him do that. I'm betting he does it from a dial-up PC at Broadwick's."

"It'd take fucking ages."

"So what?"

Warren still hadn't turned towards me. He was leaning on the bar with his elegant arms folded, lazily watching the busy barman walk up and down. I noticed how curly his lashes were, how flat his nose and perfect his ears. I wanted to touch his face with my hand, but a rigid barrier of animosity prevented me. He put his full bottom lip over his top and hummed for a count of ten.

"And that's it, huh? Wonderful. While I'm pissing about in some basement, 'e's logging in, well out of danger, probably from the comfort of 'is own home. If your poofy cousin whatisname set 'im up, there would be no problem, would there? Thought of that?"

I hadn't thought of that. It was so obvious I could have kicked myself. I could have kicked Warren for his churlishness, too. What made matters worse was that I didn't know where Eddie now lived. Then I remembered Eddie's message on my computer. He'd asked me to get in touch with him, so he must have left his phone number, possibly even an address. I tried to remember if I'd cleared out my mail-box. My computer had been smashed and junked, but the mail-box was intact, stored in some big secure computer somewhere safe from people like Warren, I hoped.

"I think I can get his number," I said, before draining my glass. "If I haven't got it, Anne will."

"No."

"What?"

"I ain't doin' it."

"You're joking," I said, staring hard at the side of his sullen face.

He turned towards me and repeated what he'd said. He wasn't joking.

"Why? C'mon, you'd love it. It's right up your street. We've done it before – remember that oil company. . ." I was stunned by his refusal. Time had been when he would have whooped and dragged me straight out the door to get his gear, after an offer like that. He had lost his sense of adventure; it had gone absent without leave, just like us.

"Leave it out, George. It's too bleedin' dangerous. This ain't fun anymore. It ain't a stupid game. They're on to you; they know you know. First your flat, then this. . ." He pointed at my face. "They'll be back. . . and pretty soon they'll be after me. These jokers have been making serious money out of this – understand? They won't let anyone mess. So don't mess no more. Cool out. Now, I'm off, unless you want to make my night."

He shrugged, patted his pocket to check his wallet and made as if to leave. I slammed my hand on the counter.

"You shit! Don't talk to me like that! You can't do this to me. You could swing it easily. It would be a great hack. What's the matter with you? Here I am sitting on the biggest damn story of my life, with the added bonus of putting one into Eddie once and for all, and you're telling me *no*? For God's sake, he's murdered someone!"

"'Xactly."

139

I turned my back on him in frustration, leaned on the bar and thrust my chin into my hand. I felt like crying with rage. He wisely waited a full minute before touching my shoulder.

"You going back to the flat?" he asked tentatively.

I controlled my temper and haughtily told him that I'd lost the keys in a little fracas hereabouts the other evening; and that, in any case, Max was expecting me.

He stood there waiting for me to look at him, for my fury to subside, as if he couldn't bear to leave on anything but an indifferent note. I ignored him, desperately trying to think of an alternative route to pin down Eddie. There was always a Plan B. There had to be.

"Have you got those printouts and the disk with the stuff from the pizza house?" I snapped, turning and facing him again.

He stood there with hands in his elegant pockets and so-what look on his pockmarked face.

"I'll have them, as soon as you can," I said.

"I've outed them. Sorry, but . . ."

I stubbed out the spent cigarette hard in the ashtray.

"Save it. In spite of all the crap we've dished out to each other lately, I thought that we were still friends . . . mates. I've been with you while you screwed around with other people's kit on umpteen occasions. You loved it. I never thought you'd bottle on this one and spoil it for me – the big one. And believe me, it is big, so big, Warren. I'm asking you. . .please."

He laughed. For the first time. The bitter-sweet sound reminded me of the pain he had been hiding.

"You always want to use me, babe. . .get some sort of favour from me. There's no give-and-take now, is there? You want to pick my brains dry, that's all. But you never listen to me, never hear what I say. I want you so bad – but you could care less. Yeh, well, sure we're friends all right, if you like, but the answer is still no. C'mon, I'll walk you home to that bleedin' office of yours and Max God Almighty *Technology Week*."

I pushed his hand away contemptuously.

140

"I bloody hate you," I said before again turning my angry back to his face as I waved at the barman. Plan B tonight was to get drunk.

"Come with me, I said." Warren's voice was low and brutal.

I ignored him and gave the barman a bigger wave. The man took some time to take my order, but as I paid, I noticed two familiar faces, one European, one oriental, reflected in the mirror behind the optics lining the bar. One nodded and the other smiled. Oh, dear me: Tweedledum and Tweedledee. I swung around quickly, hoping Warren would still be standing there, mute and shamefaced, but he had gone. I was alone in a crowded bar.

I tried to call the barman back, but he was on to another customer. The jazz band was playing another gloriously familiar tune, and the pub customers were getting louder. On any other night I would be having a great time, but now, sick with panic, I sipped slowly at the drink that I was gripping, hoping that my persecutors would think Warren was coming back. I prayed that he would, but after a quarter of an hour had passed there was no point in pretending. The pub was emptying fast: people were leaving in threes and fours. I had to get out. I slid desperately through the thinning crowd as if heading for the lavatories. There was a payphone there. It was time to call Max, if I had the time. If not, where could I hide? Where should I run to? My mind was racing; my feet were lead.

I didn't make it. The last thing I remember was being hurled through a swing-door, and a blow cracking into my skull with such tremendous, discordant force that a Chinese opera started up in my head.

There was no time left, and when I awoke, there was a strong smell of surgical spirit in my nostrils. Somebody was shining a burning light through the darkness at my aching eyes.

"Hello, love. Look straight up at me," the young black nurse said, cupping her hands over my brow and pointing her penlight at my pupils. It was painfully bright.

The stomach-gripping panic that surged up through me

as I had blinked myself awake now gave way to a shattered feeling of relief and confusion. I lifted a painful hand and touch my swollen face. My brain felt like a ball of lead swirling in a cup and I was terribly thirsty. I croaked piteously for water, but the nurse would only give me a cube of ice to suck. I'd had hangovers like this.

"Nil by mouth, until you're checked," she explained.

"What time is it?"

"Gone 12.30 am. Mmm, how do we feel?"

"I'm fine, how are you?"

She put down her penlight and gently helped me sit up. She asked me where I felt pain, and I indicated to the general area between the top of my head and my ankles. My blouse was torn and bloodstained and the heel had come off my shoe. There seemed to be a lot of noise in another cubicle and much toing and froing in the corridor. The casualty department at the Middlesex is busy at that time of night reviving damaged revellers off the street.

"We've stitched your hand for you. The X-rays are OK but you'll have to stay overnight for observation. You're concussed."

She helped me lie back on some pillows and made to leave.

"Who brought me in, nurse?"

"I'm not sure. I wasn't on shift then, but I can check if they left a name. Of course, it might have been the police, and they might want to ask you a few questions tonight or tomorrow. We had to notify them that you were obviously the victim of an assault."

"Great," I whispered, unenthusiastically. "I have to telephone someone soon. Can I do that?"

"You lie there and I'll do it for you, if you have a number?"

"No, I don't want them to know I'm here – just that I won't be back tonight. Please?"

I lay staring at my blurred bandaged hand until she brought me a telephone on a trolley. I gave her the number of *Technology Week*. She pushed in the coins, dialled, and left the receiver by my ear as I lay back on the

142

bed. It was too painful to sit up. It was also painful to speak.

Max had not been to sleep, and I presumed by the speed with which he picked up the telephone that he was still at his desk. At first he sounded concerned, but that was a momentary lapse; he was really very angry that I hadn't called sooner. Something else had happened that night. Nick had just telephoned to say that his flat had been burgled, and the place was a real mess. Nick's darkroom, with his complete library of negatives, had been destroyed in the process. I knew exactly what Nick's destructive callers had wanted – it wasn't the black marble soap-dish, to be sure.

"Where are you Georgina?" Max asked.

"I'm at . . .a friend's."

"So why are you using a payphone? Are you drunk? You sound strange."

If it didn't threaten to hurt so much, I would have screamed.

"Just tired. . .Getting the lead took longer than I expected, so I stayed over. The phone's in a corridor. Let's talk tomorrow – but I won't be in first thing."

With some effort, I reached over and replaced the receiver. It was another hour before I was wheeled down to the ward. The nurse informed me that no one had left their name at reception, and she brought in a young freckled policeman with large ears and a sandy complexion to speak to me. I told him the truth, that I couldn't remember a thing, so he left eventually and then the nurse gave me something sharp to make me sleep.

The yellowish ceiling seemed to spin as I lay in the twilight of the ward, breathing in the smell of disinfectant and the odour of fitful, sleeping bodies. The night-duty staff were talking quietly in the half-light of another room. I could just see their frilly-capped heads bobbing past an observation window. Every now and then, footsteps passed quickly along the corridors. It was difficult trying to remember what had happened, but I fought to regain an impression of what had passed. While I struggled against the drug dripping through my veins, the world I tried to

143

recall dodged in and out of the mental shadows; and memories I wanted to fend off for ever invaded my fragmented thoughts.

I dozed and I started. . .remembering trying to telephone Max. . .running and then struggling with two men while their awful fists beat down on me. No shrieking prostitutes came to rescue me this time. A mirror. . .a London voice. . .an oriental face. That was it: Chinatown. They took me into Chinatown. I remembered the smell of dripping meat on slow-turning spits, of chilli sauce and sweetmeats. Or was it Saigon? Why Saigon? Who did I know there? A frail waitress in black. No, that wasn't it – that was something else, some other time. I couldn't get a cab; Barnaby fetched me one. Poor Barnaby. I liked Barnaby. No, that was before.

Fumes, terrible fumes. London's like that – dirty. Built on centuries of debris. Loose paper, cartons and cans covering the muddy streets. Streets crammed with cars, buses and weaving messengers. Cogs and wheels. They could kill you if you stopped. . .if they caught you. Chinatown. There's always a queue for that car-park. It backs into Shaftesbury Avenue by the fire station. So many people – why didn't they help me? So tired. So sleepy. Exhausted.

That was it: exhaust fumes, the smell of damp concrete and motor oil. Eddie took me to the Grand Prix at Brands Hatch when we first met. He kissed me a lot. The noise of the engines hurt my ears. I had to cover my ears to stop the pain in my head, the awful pain in my head. There had been a bad start. Crumpled metal. No one hurt. But me, I had a pain in my head. Someone was wrenching at my hair, scraping my face along the hard floor, and the sweet, sick smell of musky aftershave came creeping over me. It was a message, a secret message for me in a jangle of pocket change.

I started at the sound of the ward doors opening and closing. It was raining hard outside. A gutter was clogged, and water poured down on to the outside sill. Someone was writing something on a clipboard, which they then hung at the foot of my bed. My father had a clipboard. Very organised. Very upright. So did Julian. Poor silly Julian. Eddie, my husband, killed Julian, my cousin. They were friends for so long. So long, Julian. Oh, Eddie. . .I loved Eddie. I did. No, I loved someone else. . .but who?. . .I couldn't remember. Someone was singing. "Swing it, swing it."

So cruel. My boy took my hand and cut it. No. I put my hand up, that's how it happened. I gave my hand to Warren, but he had a knife; he had come towards me with a knife. A Swiss Army knife? No, it had a shiny long, sharp blade: a flicknife. Why was he killing me? Warren was my friend. No. Who was singing?

"When the shark has had his dinner there is blood upon his fins, but Macheath he had his gloves on: they say nothing of his sins." Who has pearly white teeth? The shark. Why was there someone singing all the time? Was it me?

Warren came towards me with a knife. Or was it towards them? I put my hand up to the blade. The pain – I couldn't breathe with the terrible pain. They were killing me. Yes, my hand caught the blade. Metallic blood in my teeth. Where was Warren? Where was my friend?

There was a rattle like the sound of a refrigerator switching off.

"Tea. . .Morning. . .Tea."

An hour and a half later, I gently, and lightheadedly, reached for the locker. Miraculously, my bag was inside along with my tattered clothes. They would have to do until I could get to the shops. This trip was costing me a fortune. I leaned back drowsily as another nurse took my temperature.

"Can I go?"

"No. Doctor has to check the wound."

"Is that it?"

"You've had a bad knock to the head. Your hand is in poor shape. We have to do more tests. You can't go."

"Ah, but I have to," I said wearily.

"Let me dress that wound, now, silly girl."

When she had finished, I drew the curtains around

my bed and painfully removed the bloodstained back-to-front heavy cotton gown that I had slept in. I checked my bag: the photograph was still inside with some keys. They looked like the keys to Warren's flat but I couldn't remember where I had got them from.

There was a small mirror inside the locker door. I hardly recognised the image in it; my swollen, woebegone face with fresh scratches and bluish bruises stared mournfully back at me. I wanted to lie down and cry, but I didn't have the time.

It took more nerve to walk out of that ward than I ever thought I had. Nice middle-class girls don't do that sort of thing. Crazy drunks, fighting boys, mental cases, junkies, juvenile delinquents, hysterical mothers, the senile and suicides did. They walked, ran and jumped their way out, every day of the week, with no regard for good breeding or hospital regulations. It takes real fear, courage, or madness to disobey Matron.

It was raining hard in the street outside. My soaking hair and clothes made my shabby appearance much, much worse. Three cafés selling croissants turned me away, but I managed a cup of sweet tea and buttered toast in a greasy spoon near Oxford Street. I had no money but there was a quiver of plastic cards in my bag, so by ten o'clock I was by the glass doors of a large chain store in Oxford Street waiting for them to open.

My head ached and my hand throbbed mercilessly as I dressed myself in new underwear, new Levis, a cream sweater, a black denim jacket and camel-coloured desert boots as well. I'd chosen them for durability rather than fashion, and as such they had a certain style.

My battered image, cruelly repeated in the changing-room's multiple mirrors, swam sickeningly as I stood grappling with the buttons of my jeans. The ageing yellow and mauve bruises on my face stood out like old love bites. The new bruises stained my temples, and the now permanent shadows under my eyes had deepened in my grey, drawn face. I needed some heavy make-up, and the young girl who brought it to me asked if I felt all right. I lied to her, but she didn't believe me. She also brought me some water and two aspirins, and took my old clothes away in a bag.

As I sat on the changing-room bench, carefully sipping the cold liquid, I thought again about Warren. It was so difficult trying to remember. I knew that somehow I'd been taken to a car-park and beaten. There was an engine running, and the suffocating stench of fumes in my face blocked my breath. There was blackness all around as I choked and fought. The foul language might have been mine. I couldn't understand why Warren was there with a knife. I remembered the blade catching my hand. Blood spurted like warm sauce onto my face and my blouse, but it wasn't mine, I was sure it wasn't mine. He must have cut someone else. Or did someone cut him? I sat alone on the bench, confused and afraid – afraid for him, and guilty. The guilt in me ached almost as much as my head, stung almost as much as my hand.

I fought back the tears. It was all my fault. Plan B. There still had to be a Plan B to get us out of this; but first I had to go to the office to see Max.

There were only a few people hanging around when I eventually reached the office. It was publication day, so no one really needed to hurry in. Their faces registered what I looked like, but I gave no encouragement for anyone to come near.

Max sat quite still in his chair, his lips tight and shrewlike.

"You stupid little fool," he said, as I sat down.

"Thanks. Just what I need after the sort of night I've had. Sympathy, comfort, encouragement. . ."

He softened just a little, and inquired what had happened. With, for him, an extraordinarily human gesture, he tapped his pale hand on mine in sympathy, while staring away at some far point in the office.

I told him all I could remember.

"I think we'll have to call the City police now," Max interrupted briskly. "We'll call the Stock Exchange in any case. They'll investigate and pass it on to the Securities and Investment Board for what it's worth. More than likely the DTI will come in straight away. Got any names?"

"What good will that do? The plug will be pulled, and we'll never pin the bastards down. Anyway, the police have already spoken to me about the assault. I told them I couldn't remember anything. . . which was quite true when they spoke to me."

I didn't want to lose Eddie now, when I was so close. Max had to do the *right* thing, but I didn't want to.

"Georgina, I have to tell you that this morning I spoke to Mr Piggott at Pull-Up For Pizza. Julian's files are still intact. However, there is no record of any extraneous code or program in the system."

"To what level?"

"At any level he's reached. Mr Piggott is most perturbed. Deleting to such a degree leaves its own mark, proof of penetration itself, as you well know. He's investigating."

It meant my story was falling apart. There was no proof of the message that had killed Julian. Also Warren had junked the printouts, which would be meaningless now anyway. The negatives of the photograph had gone. All I had left was the Lifestyle connection and a list of directors. It was all too tenuous.

"It's not over, Georgina. There's still a good story to write, if there's an investigation. God, girl, you look awful. . .terrible. I don't want you to work today. Go somewhere and sleep, – upstairs if you like. See how you feel later."

Max's peremptory voice was sliding away. I got up, without a word, and walked away from him to my disorderly paper-strewn desk.

The latest issue of *Technology Week* lay crisp and shiny on top of a large pile of the day's newspapers and releases. On the front page was Nick's picture of grey-faced dealers watching red-faced computer screens along with my story about Broadwick & Klein's successful computer system and the looming problem of other firms' computer systems crumbling under the strain.

It was Friday – a week since Warren and I had gone to Julian's cottage. It was the end of a two-week account period for share dealers. Brokers' and banks' back office settlement computers on both sides of the Atlantic would be working overtime to take the strain of massive additional trading turnover that had taken place during the crash. In the US, settlement had to take place in seven days; in the UK it was ten, so it would be a Monday, this Monday, the first in November, when the City would feel the first real blast of what promised to be a long hard winter.

UK firms had still been trying to sort out the backlog on the British Government's huge privatisation issues. With the crash as well, they would be disappearing under a mountain of paper. Firms were already unclear about who bought, and who sold, and at how much, when the pace was at its most hectic. It was a good story, especially since I'd received the first whiff of job cuts in the City as computer projects were cancelled. We'd covered the breakdown of SEAQ, too, and there was a speculative piece on program trading.

Mary Stow had done well with a story on a major computer company losing a million-pound order as a major broker cancelled equipment in an immediate cutback after suffering huge losses. Charlie hadn't contributed much, and as I scanned the City analysis inside I wondered how much he'd raised to meet his debt. I knew I had my future to consider as well. Max wouldn't forget about the investment club.

As I flicked through the paper, the phone rang.

"It's me." Warren's dry voice crackled down the line and I caught my breath. My depression lifted in a moment.

"Oh, thank God," I whispered, close to tears again. "I didn't know what had happened to you. Are you hurt? Where are you?"

"I'm OK. I rang the 'ospital. They said you discharged

yourself. . . stupid, so stupid, as ever. . .Never mind, you OK? God, I thought you were dead."

"I am, sort of."

"Pretty bad, huh?"

"Put it this way, I hadn't had such a bang since. . ."

"Oh, you're so bleedin' crude." He laughed a little with relief, and a brief familiar memory of times past eased the pain.

We paused together before bumbling our simultaneous self-conscious apologies, and then stopped again, as if embarrassed to discover the closeness of our voices and the distance of our mouths.

"Are you OK? Tell me what happened. I can only remember a little bit," I said, breaking the awkward silence.

He said he had a couple of bruised ribs. He'd been worried about me and, despite what I had said, he had waited for me to leave the pub, to check that I got back to Max's safely. The next thing he knew I was on the street and he was separated from me by the dispersing crowd. The two men had propped me between them like a drunken playmate, and dragged me five hundred yards to the lift of a car-park in Chinatown. He'd managed to follow and had seen them beating me into a waiting car. His words brought back the strong oily smell of car fumes and the tickety-tick of an engine.

"I steamed in, but I caught your 'and wiv me knife in the ruck. I got one of the geezers in the shoulder – the Chink. I didn't really 'urt him bad, nicked him more than anyfin', but there was blood all over the fucking place. Christ, I didn't know what to do. They were killing you."

Warren's voice was beginning to crack up. It broke down my resistance and I started to cry.

"I didn't know you carried a knife, Warren," I snivelled, searching in my bag for something to wipe my nose.

"Yeh, well I don't, but where I come from you know how to use one. I prefer a cosh in the cab – well, under the seat as a rule, know what I mean? But things have been a bit unusual recently, yeh? You'd agree with that, wouldn't

150

you? Look, you should have stayed in the 'ospital. No one but me knew you were there."

He apologised again, but I stopped him.

"Oh, Warren, You warned me. My story's busted. Nick's place was turned over for the negatives, and the message in the pizza house has been totally lifted. Barnaby won't say a word. So what have I got? A list of directors of Lifestyle and Kirren Ventures. So what? Max will probably call in the police now, so that's it. I'll give them what I've got."

Warren said nothing to that. He didn't even say that he'd told me so.

"I love you," he said instead, quietly, seriously, breaking the painful silence. "No matter what's happened, what you said, what I said, or what I done."

The words had come without warning. I blinked my eyes as if in bright sunlight, and the tears dropped down my nose and onto the my grubby desk. Suddenly I felt foolish and vulnerable.

"Can I see you?" I asked, sniffing and fiddling nervously with the cord of the telephone.

"I. . .I don't want to meet you. Not for a while. . . I'll be in touch, I promise. Don't worry, I'll be in touch, for sure." He tried to sound brisk and efficient but his voice did not reassure me.

As the line went dead, the pain in my chest gnawed at me. There was nothing sure, nothing safe. I dreaded the thought that he had lied, that he had killed that man and it wasn't over at all. He was hiding. Warren was in trouble and I sat staring miserably at the telephone, knowing it was all my fault. I couldn't bear the responsibility of hurting Warren anymore.

Mary Stow chose a careful moment to approach me. I had gone to the ladies' toilet to weep, and locked myself in a cubicle. First she stood outside waiting. After a while she coughed and called my name. I told her to go away, but she waited and coughed again.

After five more minutes I opened the door and dealt her

a ferocious red-eyed scowl, before walking to the basin to dab my face with toilet tissue.

"What do you want?" I snapped, once I'd gathered some composure.

"Are you all right?" she bleated.

"Yes, wonderful. Now what is it that's so damn important?" I said scornfully to her reflection as I leaned towards the mirror, feeling a tender, fresher bruise on my temple. She was holding a sheaf of notes nervously against her concave chest.

"The research Max asked me to do – would it be of any use to you now?"

Wearily I turned to her and nodded. She was only doing her job; and very well she did it, too, by all accounts. Good research, persistent as a summer fly – a little naive, but that would wear off after a few kicks in the rear. She briefed me on what Max had asked her to do. I knew most of it already.

Nothing had seemed amiss. Come the crash, everyone – analysts, market makers and dealers alike – were all pushing to sell.

"Wall Street indicated that a big 'correction' was about to happen. It had sunk already the day before, and when London opened, it was off 150 points, Hong Kong had to close, and then there was Tokyo. . ."

"We know all this," I interrupted.

"Just setting the scene. . ." she replied with a show of spirit.

"Well, I rang around the City analysts, and the sort of replies I got were rather similar: Wall Street's reaction to the September trade deficit, the falling unsupported dollar, interest rates up elsewhere, the top analyst/chartist Rechter posting a *sell* message followed by computer-driven selling by the big US pension and mutual funds. Nothing wrong with our economy or our securities, but plenty wrong over the pond."

"Yes, OK," I said, leaning against the basin.

"The thing that struck me most, though, was that every single person I spoke to said they had moved on their instincts, not on any of this" – she waved her notes – "but on a gut feeling that it was time to sell, even though there seemed to be more steam left in the bull market at the time. I think it's important, especially considering that we don't have computerised trading over here and yet the slide here was just as bad as on Wall Street. Everyone is adamant that program trading, in particular, pushed the market in the US. Finally, I dug out this interview with Rechter in the *Washington Post*. He said his charts indicated a correction, but not at that time. He also says here" – she pointed to a cutting – "that he just had a gut feel to publish that *sell* message."

This girl had a nose for a story, I thought, appreciatively, looking down at my plastic Swatch watch. New York was about six hours behind which meant I could catch him in about an hour – at our lunchtime, his coffee-break. He'd have been up at least two hours by then, being one of the originators of the breakfast-time power business meeting for which we journalists bore him an eternal grudge.

"Mary, you're a star," I said, grasping her shoulders.

"Would you like an aspirin?" she inquired sympathetically.

CHAPTER TWELVE

PETER RECHTER IS A MAN who moves markets and aptly fulfils the American dream that even the poor, fat and ugly can become rich and, thus, desirable. A tough New Yorker in his forties, he had stores of immense power and charisma. This is wonderful good fortune for someone with the face and stature of a primate. Suits sagged at the very sight of him. Physically he may have been a little further down our evolutionary scale, but mentally he was a good eon's leap in front.

Historical notes state that he was the only son among four daughters, and left a Brooklyn school at sixteen, held two degrees in business and economics by the time he was twenty-five, made his first million a year later, and millions exponentially every since. He'd been married for successive, if brief, periods of time to four beautiful women and, by all accounts, had fathered five children.

I called him on a day and in an age when proud men with Rolex watches on each arm jumped at his command, scampering around like anxious mutts for scraps from the great man's table. Fund managers fêted him and small investors preceded every instruction to their broker with his name. If Rechter said sell, they sold, and markets fell. If Rechter said buy, they bought, and markets rose. If his stomach ached, Wall Street held on to its trousers.

I would have felt less comfortable telephoning him had his cuttings not indicated that he obviously loved women. Society photographs caught him entering theatres and expensive restaurants with his stubby arm around the slinky hips of tall, fair women. He couldn't see my face but I still had my voice, so I knew he would at least talk to me, if only for the entertaining diversion of intercontinental social intercourse. His conversational skills underlined the fact that he let money talk.

"Mr Rechter?"

"Why, hello there. Georgina Powers? What a lovely name! And what a wonderful English accent!"

"Thank you. Mr Rechter. . .I wondered. . . would you mind. . .I'm a computer journalist doing a story on the crash. I wondered . . . could you please help me?"

Playing my part as the distressed gentlewoman, I was all but fluttering my eyelashes, and, for all I knew, I might have been, but my face was too numb for me to tell. Rechter was charming in his way, flirting sweetly and teasing me harmlessly, though revealing little new information. He repeated almost word for word what he had said to the *Washington Post*.

"And you say it was a gut feel, almost a premonition? Fascinating! You do use a computer though, for charting and so forth, don't you?" I twittered, wheedling all the while.

"Sure, all the time. I've got a DRAC for the office number crunching with a networked PC attached. You wanna know the configuration, honey?"

"Well, actually, I wondered if you could do an audit."

"Eh. . .Sure. What the hell for?"

"Well, Mr Rechter, I think you've been hacked, and in the process you have been, er. . . had."

"You cannot be serious."

"I am, I'm afraid."

"Oh, shit, shit, shit!"

He was open-minded enough not to put the receiver down when I said what to look for. I told him that if he found the bizarre program I described, then he was the innocent party in a conspiracy to crash the world markets.

"This little bit of mind poison come from L.A.?"

"Milton Keynes, actually."

He grunted in disbelief. I gave him the office telephone number at the flat. The folksy sugar-daddy charm disappeared like melting spun candy. I was to tell no one I had called, and he would phone me within six hours. If I was right, he would discuss then what we should do with the information. After a curt and polite goodbye, the line went dead.

I leaned back in my chair and breathed out with satisfaction. I had a story, I had the photograph, I had Lifestyle, I surely had the program. Now for Eddie.

My mailbox didn't have his number or his address. I must have junked it. So I called Anne.

"Tell him we want what he took back," she muttered after she'd given me what I wanted. "I think that's where he said he lives most of the time. He's got more than one place, you know."

I closed my eyes with frustration and prayed that I didn't have to track down all his ill-gotten property. The cut in my hand jabbed a shot of pain up through my arm. I'd been hurt, but I wasn't frightened anymore. I had him.

"You better believe it," I said to myself before getting up and making my way to Max. I was embarrassed to see Nick by his side, resplendent in his chunky black motorcycle leathers.

"The negatives are here," said Max. Nick had left them in the studio on file. He showed me the wallet with three negatives marked at the side. They had the message on them. Despite his anger at his own misfortune, Nick seemed eager to please, relieved that something had been saved for me. I reported to them my conversation with Rechter. If he came good, we had a great story, but without the protagonists – they would come later. Max couldn't disguise the pleasure in his eyes. It was good enough for *Technology Week*, but not for me. I wanted blood for the killing of Julian, my sudden ill health, and Warren's fugitive status. I wanted Fisher and Eddie.

"I'm going to inform the Stock Exchange's surveillance team, and tell them what to look for. Question is, do we give them names yet?" said Max.

"No," I said firmly, "because we haven't got them yet. Just let them know they have a problem."

It was fortunate that the City was having a slow time that afternoon, for at 2.00 pm precisely several thousand computer screens went blank.

At 4.00 pm Rechter called me at the office. He'd found the program. He was stung by its implications: what it had meant to Wall Street and beyond. Since he hadn't breached any law, but was a man with a sense of social responsibility, he made a deal with me. He would record the evidence and then remove it from his system, but he would only go public and risk his reputation if everyone else did. It was the first indication I had that not every victim would pull together on this story. Victims of computer insecurity were as reluctant as rape victims to talk about it – exposure of their weakness being almost as terrible to bear as the crime itself. If there was one thing worse than being had by a hacker, it was being seen to be have been had by a hacker.

Rechter's proposition sounded reasonable, until at 4.30 pm the Stock Exchange's most senior manager of information services called to inform us that there had been a thorough check of the system and no breach had been discovered. Every bit and byte had been accounted for; there was no program in the system such as the one we had described.

I cursed with frustration. The system was clean. Either someone had wiped over their tracks, or the Stock Exchange data-processing guys were lying; and the latter was a strong possibility.

"I wish I understood all this," said Nick irritably as gloom spread across our faces. Max kept slapping his hand impatiently on the armrest of his chair.

"I need to rest," I said, after a minute's silence. Max looked at me, but I shook my aching head. I said I wanted to go to my flat – my new flat. I walked over to my desk and, opening a drawer, took out my tape-recorder.

"Let me take you. I've got the bike." Nick stood by my desk tapping his black and red gauntlets against the palm of his hand.

"No, thanks. You've got your own place to worry about.

I'll take a cab," I replied, walking away briskly with my things. He followed me to the lift and took my good arm.

"Please, I want to help you. Don't keep pushing me away. You're blocking me out."

"Who's pushed who?" I said bitterly. Then I relented, placing my bandaged hand on his wrist. "It doesn't matter now, really. I don't need your help. I like you. . .really. . .a lot, but I want to be by myself now. Thanks."

The lift door opened and he held the call button pressed in. As he stood there, his thick black leathers creaked like the branches of an olive tree in a hot summer breeze. His glossy dark hair was untidy, his eyes intense. I wanted to put my leg around him and kiss him on the mouth.

"Thank you?" I asked with some self-control, nodding at the doors.

He took his hand from the button and the doors closed. If I had left like this at any other time, I would have crumpled and begged him to take me home, wrap his arms around me and soothe my troubles away. But that wasn't where I was going. I had to get to Broadwick & Klein before five.

Every cab that passed in the street reminded me of Warren, and I hoped that he was safe. I wanted him to be at the flat, if and when I got there. I wanted us to go back to where we were before we'd stumbled on that program in Julian's PC.

As I pushed through the cold pompous portals of Broadwick's, the slick and shiny receptionist stared mercilessly at my battered face.

"Can I help you?" she enquired as if there could be no remote possibility of that.

"Eddie Powers."

"And who shall I say. . ."

"His wife," I snarled. "And give him this." I handed the photograph to her and she passed it to a security guard. He went straight to the lift.

After quarter of an hour on the curved leather seating, the black security guard stepped forward and escorted me to the glass pump elevator. I lost count of the floors, and as the lift sighed to a stop, we stepped out on unfamiliar terrain. As we trod silently along a grey carpeted corridor, I wondered what part of the building we could be in. The guard pushed open a walnut door with his gloved hand. As I entered, Kay Fisher sat opposite me, serenely balanced on the edge of a wide metallic desk.

"My, my, you do look ill," she remarked as the door shut behind me and we were left alone.

"I came to see my husband," I said, turning to go.

"Yes, he told me, but he's a little busy. He'll be here later I thought we could have a little talk first. You don't mind do you?"

She eased herself off the table and pointed to a uphol-stered steel chair. When I was seated she turned and walked around the desk to her own barely more substantial chair. The room was more like a small conference room than an office. It was sparsely but fashionably furnished in the lean uncluttered design-conscious look of the day. A small, leafy potted plant stood on a tall, thin lonely table in a corner by a wide-arched tinted window. It was dark outside.

I said nothing while we waited, and she appraised me, her white folded hands reflected in the black sheen of the desk. I grew impatient and looked at my watch.

"He's told me about the photograph, but I really don't know what you want us to say?" she said at last, smoothing a microscopic speck from the front of her blue suit.

"I want you to explain it." As I spoke, one of the room doors opened, and two tough-looking, crop-haired men walked in: the balding Londoner and the Japanese, his arm in a sling. What little was in my stomach turned to water.

"There appears to be a smudge on the photograph which forms the word 'BUY', so Eddie tells me. Why should I have to explain it?"

Her eyes glittered with rancour, and I could feel a film of perspiration forming under my arms and across my chest. She got up again and moved on her needle-sharp shoes to the front of the desk.

"I know about Kirren Ventures," I said, shifting my position and crossing my legs in an effort to appear casual and confident. She raised a discreet and admonishing eyebrow. Its effect was like a short sharp rap on the knuckles.

"Well, that's going to upset a whole string of people. What shall we do with you?" she sighed.

It was my turn to cut her up. I shrugged.

"Nothing else, I hope. My recovery period is getting shorter all the time. Why risk all that money on half a story that a poor hack like me might have? Of course, I've got photographs. . .including the negatives, directors' names, Rechter's system backed up, a dead cousin, a suspicious pizza house – all stored and secured. And now the Stock Exchange is looking for the program that gave us all that smudgy little message. . . well, SIB and SEC investigations have to follow, if I keep it up. It's only a matter of time."

There were no smiles at all now and the room seemed to shrink a little, as if the walls and windows were inching forwards to crush me. It was close. I felt as if someone was holding a damp, warm sponge over my face. I cleared my throat and spoke slowly and deliberately.

"I could, however, be persuaded to give it all up, lose my notes, and research something else for a while. I'm a bit short at the moment. . ."

She still didn't smile. Her patience for the little game she had begun was evaporating like precious water from a dead sea. She didn't seem to care what I claimed to have. I began to estimate my chances in reaching the door I'd come in by, when suddenly it opened and Eddie appeared, looking annoyed and agitated.

"George, you're here. God, you look awful! What's going on?" he said walking to Ms Fisher's desk and slinging the photograph across it. He came over to my chair and placed his large hands on the back of it. I didn't know whether to be pleased to see him or not. I suddenly felt as if it ought to be the former.

"Your wife has been telling me what she knows, for what it's worth, Eddie dear. She seems to think she has something on us, actually. I can't imagine what. . .but you know the press and their wild stories."

Eddie looked down grim-faced at me and then over at her, but she nothing.

"I don't like you, Miss Powers. You've been messing in my yard and I want you out. You say you're a bit short of money. How much would you like to research another story?" she continued at last.

I was relieved that she'd started talking money and not pounds of flesh. The day had begun to seem very long indeed. My hand was draining energy from me, and I began to feel weak. The adrenalin that had sustained me was ebbing away fast. Eddie stood tensely by my chair.

"Oh. . . fifty grand in cash or similar, please," I replied, waving my good hand magnanimously in the air.

"Is that *all*?" She looked at me almost kindly. Well she might – the figure was probably a third of her basic salary, and a decimal point of what she and Eddie had produced between them.

"It's not for me. It's for a friend. And, by the way, this should also mean that you leave me alone – and my partner, Warren Graham."

Her face turned to stone. One of her silent cohorts, the Londoner, left the room and returned minutes later with what seemed to be a large cheque. There was silence as Kay Fisher took a gold pen from the inside top pocket of her suit, leaned over the desk and scratched something on the paper, along with her signature, her auburn hair glinting in the spotlights that beamed from the low ceiling. She handed the paper to the same man who had fetched it, and he walked over and handed it to me with a small, courteous bow.

My experience of instruments of finance was not very extensive. I assumed it was a bond because it said so. In any case, I wouldn't have cared if it had been Monopoly money, I wanted out of there.

I stood up, folded the paper and tucked it into my bag, before snapping it shut. Turning to Eddie, I gave him a wry half-smile. He did not look amused.

161

The room maintained its deadly, oppressive silence as I left, closing the door firmly behind me with a loud click. The arguing began almost immediately. I leaned up against the door as every good journalist should, and heard Eddie shouting about who the hell had roughed me up, then I heard something about "that black bastard" which I took be mean Warren.

"You vindictive bitch! You'll ruin everything for a shit story she can't prove," roared Eddie, to which Fisher screamed something about Kirren Ventures and wanting "her" – which I took to mean me – "out of the way, permanently".

I heard a chair fall over. There was a scuffling, grunting noise, and the light, quick sound of a hand-made pure cotton shirt tearing. I'd already decided to head for the lift when the door flew open and Eddie ran out. His lip was bleeding and his smooth hair was ruffled. It was *his* shirt that was ruined.

"You still here? Aw, shit, come on, you stupid fool!" he growled, shoving and dragging me along and through a side door. It was the Gents. We were panting, myself with fear and he with fury, as he held his large hand over my mouth. There was a tap dripping: it sounded to me like Niagara Falls. I heard footsteps hurrying along the corridor. One man was obviously in pain, and Fisher was snapping instructions like an unpleasant terrier. Eddie made a hushing shape with his lips. I was confused but I obeyed him.

"You ready for this?" he whispered eventually. I nodded and he hauled open the door again and ran in the opposite direction from the lift, dragging me along by my good arm. As we reached the end of the corridor, he opened yet another door. We were on the seventh floor and facing the fire escape.

We hadn't gained much time. When we reached the fourth floor, the leathery footsteps following us were close behind and gaining. I was beginning to stumble; the downwards spiralling steps were making me feel dizzier than I felt already. My new boots slipped on a piece of paper and glided over two steps, then as I staggered to keep my balance, I fell against the wall. My tape-recorder bounced out of my belt and on down the stairs.

Eddie tried to steady me but the men were now upon us, grabbing at his arms. He used his height and weight to shrug one off, but he didn't see the gun. The Japanese held it in his left hand, pointing at my head. He glanced desperately at me and then at Eddie. Eddie was too preoccupied with the Londoner to notice.

"Get up the stairs, you! You!" said my would-be attacker, frantically kicking me with his foot. Eddie couldn't disentangle himself, even though I was sure that was why the Japanese guy had pulled the gun. He wasn't holding it with any confidence, and was clearly not used to handling one.

I couldn't believe the bungling fool would a fire a gun on the well-lit stairwell of a major securities house in the middle of the City – not with all those glass windows as well. Given their record to date, I had a strong feeling this pair were not experienced hit-men.

Unsure of what to do next, the Japanese then pointed the weapon desperately at Eddie. I screamed a warning and Eddie twisted round, pulling his cursing opponent between him and the man with the gun. The Londoner lost his balance and fell backwards, taking Eddie with him. Their considerable combined weights crushed the bandaged right shoulder of the trapped Japanese gunman. He hollered in agony as they pressed on the wound which Warren had inflicted on him.

The gun clattered onto the steps and skidded through the railings. We heard the sound of its uneven descent to the ground floor.

Eddie took his chance and swung his fists about until the exhausted Londoner released him, slumping back again on his howling friend.

I staggered to my feet, looking desperately around for my tape-recorder. It had gone the way of the gun. Eddie grabbed me and we ran. There was a door on each floor and tearing open the one at the third level, Eddie pushed me into a large, sparsely populated dealing room. Someone waved amicably at Eddie as we walked briskly across the floor between banks of screens towards some swing-doors. Once through them, we travelled rapidly along a curved corridor to the central glass tube lift. Within three minutes we were out and onto the wet, well-lit street, walking fast towards Liverpool Street.

"Can't go to my place, can't go to yours. Is your office safe? What about a hotel?" said Eddie as we clambered into a cab.

"There's my friend Warren's place – is that safe? Is he safe?"

"Oh, yeah, he's safe . . . but his place might not be now." He then leant forward to instruct the cabbie. "The Tower."

As we drove through the pouring rain, at one point Eddie stopped the cab for a minute and came back soaked to the skin but carrying hot salt-beef and mustard sandwiches. It was as if we were travelling back through time.

"Eat," he said.

"She's Macheath, for sure," I said, chewing slowly with my eyes closed.

It was freezing cold and still raining heavily when we finally arrived at the hotel. The normally fifteen-minute journey had taken twenty-five because of the rush-hour traffic. I remember Eddie paying the cabbie, and the damp muddy smell of river drifting into my nostrils as I leaned on his arm.

It was early evening and the hotel foyer was busy. People were coming down to the softly-lit restaurants and carvery to eat. Women wore shiny, tight black dresses like silvery wet-suits. Hotel staff scurried about in drummer-boy uniforms, glancing at me as I stood alone on the red checked carpet by the lifts. Despite my new clothes, I must have looked like a vagrant to the well-heeled tourists and business people who passed me. A porter asked where my bags were. I pointed at Eddie, who was negotiating at the reception desk, and moved off to sit at a writing table tucked beside a group of sumptious chairs in the reception area. I took the bond from my pocket and slipped it in an envelope, then in a wobbly left-handed scrawl I wrote Charlie's name and his address in Earls Court. I handed it with some change to a passing drummer-boy.

"Make sure you post it," I said.

"Yes, madam."

After about ten minutes Eddie came looking for me.

"I've got the honeymoon suite. . .sweetie," he said. Grinning amiably and taking my arm, he guided me to the lift.

"Your bags, sir?" said a hovering porter, with the merest hint of innuendo.

"Aah. . . later, I hope," drawled Eddie. "We've had a few problems getting ourselves here, y'know. Take this. . ." The money changed hands. "Room 551. A bottle of champagne, smoked salmon sandwich platter, and some fruit. Strawberries – do you have them?"

"Jet fresh from Israel, sir."

"Great, and don't forget the cream. How long?"

"Twenty minutes, sir."

He nodded and left. The lift doors slid open and we stepped in.

"What's it all about, Eddie?"

"You tell me, kid. You tell me."

We sat for a long while, recuperating in silence. I had a lot to ask, but somehow the warmth of the room, its gentle lights, the softness of the wide bed, the weakness in me, and the dull pain lulled me to sleep. I awoke suddenly when something cracked like a gun.

Eddie stood shamefacedly across the large room by a plush pink armchair. He had a bottle of champagne in his hands. The television was on low.

"Aah. . . sorry. I've been staring at this for two hours now."

I sat up, rubbing my eyes and then my mouth.

"I'm thirsty. What time is it?"

"Nine."

"Turn over for the news."

There was a piece about the crash at the end of the programme, which included brief details of the Stock Exchange computers failing that afternoon, and a short piece on proposed curbs in "program trading", giving the impression that the world's financial computers had all but taken over. There was nothing else relevant.

"What did you expect, honey?" said Eddie, handing me a glass of champagne. The bubbles bounced off my nose.

"Nothing," I answered morosely, putting the glass down and awkwardly propping up some pillows behind my back.

Eddie drained his glass and filled it again. Then he took off his loosened tie, undid his ripped shirt and began to undress.

"I'm going to have a shower," he said, strolling into the bathroom with his glass. When I heard the water gushing, I picked up the telephone and waited for an outside line.

"Max? It's Georgina. I'm at the Tower. . .by the river. Look, there is something I'm going to sort out, now. If I don't call back within two hours, call the police. This is to do with my cousin's death."

"Glad to hear you're OK. All right, be careful."

I put the champagne glass down and poured myself some water from a jug. Max hadn't sounded surprised. He *should* have been surprised, but then I could never count on a normal reaction from him. I drank two full glasses of water and went back to bed with the champagne. Leaning back on the peach-coloured pillows, I listened to the water running fast into the bath, then emptying down the drain. Imagine it draining all that way, I thought. Imagine how many holes people emptied dirty water down in this city. All those separate pipes joining up somewhere underground. All that water getting cleaned up, recycled, pumped back up again for us to use again and again. Nothing was ever really pure and clean, not at the beginning, nor at the end. It was always tainted, always muddied, and we all drank from the same cup.

I looked miserably at my grubby bandaged hand. It was

sticky and hot in the room. I stood up, this time to slide open a window. The thick, tinted glass would only open a fraction as I tired – not enough to get my nose through, never mind my aching head. The management obviously didn't want people selfishly flinging themselves out. Suicide is so bad for the hotel trade.

London was drenched in a haze of sodium orange drizzle. The tall turrets of Tower Bridge stood darkly at either side of the gloomy river. The thin draught of cold damp night air was refreshingly cool against my face. Peering through the glass, I could see just make out the rebuilt riverfront on the south side. The fresh stone facades of prestigious office buildings glistened like well-kept warehouses unsullied by winches, ropes and hefty sacks of sugar or jute, loaded and heaved up against them on worn wooden pallets. Their commodity was money. They shone clean, new and smooth in their own self-indulgent spotlights, and the greyish brown river was quiet beside them.

A floating disco/bar smoothed past bearing an office party towards the white cowls of the Thames barrier. People were laughing and drinking under the multicoloured lights. A police launch skipped towards Westminster, and there came and went the watery sound of greasy spray whipping away from heavy wheels that thundered across the bridge. Taxis splashed through puddles as they rounded the hotel for quick business at the foyer. The sound of a London taxi is very distinctive: the rumbling tick of its diesel engine, the steady shift of the gears.

From my grubby flat in Bow, I would have seen countless lights shining brightly through cheap net curtains coyly hung for privacy and respectability across the repetitive square windows of the tower blocks. Every now and then the dim rosy glow of a coloured bulb would punctuate this digital procession of lights. The sheer concrete walls would have already soaked in the rain to form huge dark patches of weeping damp. The noise would be different, too. No soft voices in carpeted corridors, no resonant clatter of a glass in another room. In my block you heard the clang of pots and pans, something falling on a bare floor, loud music, fights. Sometimes a woman shrieked with laughter. She likely had a warm black voice, the sort you'd imagine on a wooden porch under a red Jamaican sky. The rhythm would drum through the walls, across the dark walkways and the parked jumble of cars. Dum-diddy-dum, diddy-dum, diddy-diddy-dum. Reggae and the spicy henna smell of dark curry would waft up and in through the damp, ill-fitting windows.

Parties, weekend parties. People in bedrooms and kitchens, eating, drinking, dancing, smoking and screwing around. That's how I had met Eddie, in a kitchen at a party, but not in the East End. Instead somewhere west, south of the river, by the river. . .

I turned, hearing Eddie come into the room behind me, a towel wrapped around his waist. The dark hair on his chest and stomach glistened with moisture. He was paler than I remembered him. There was a large dark bruise on his arm, and another surrounding a cut on his leg where he had been kicked. He lifted up his trousers and checked his pockets.

"Going somewhere?" I asked.

"To California, maybe," he said, pulling on his trousers.

"Why?"

"I'm finished with this city, and I have a business to run."

"Julian's business?"

He paused and folded his arms across his wide chest, setting himself apart, bracing himself for what was to come at him.

"Our business. He'd have wanted me to do this."

"What about Kirren Ventures?"

"What about it?"

"You and Fisher have been dealing in a customer account in which you have an undeclared interest. Naughty, naughty – Broadwick & Klein won't like that. The SIB won't like it, and nor will the SEC. Misdemeanours in a US securities establishment – not procedure. You'll never work in this City again. You'll never work on Wall Street. You could even go to jail. They'll certainly sting you for some of that wonderful money you think such a lot of."

168

"I couldn't care less about the City and Wall Street, I'm not going to jail, and as for money. . ." he laughed ". . . however big the fine, we'd have more that plenty left over to live on. If you knew how much we made – I made – you might not be that keen to divorce me. 'Course, there's alimony, I forgot, but you might not get that much what with the two-year separation and all. . ."

I was not to be put off by his smugness.

"OK. They might, just might let you off lightly for a bit of sharp practice, Eddie, but not for the message. They'll never forgive you for the message that caused the big crash. It did, didn't it? Little old ladies, people's mothers, Eddie, they lost their life savings. The funds took a bath; big investors, maybe even the Mafia, lost their laundry. Someone somewhere is going to keep coming after you. You'll have to be looking at different options and different futures now, won't you? Where are you going to hide?"

Eddie looked hard at me, shrugged, zipped up his fly and started to buckle his belt.

"That was an accident. It shouldn't have happened. . .we kind of yelled at an avalanche. Anyway, prove it was me. Prove the connection between me and the message. I lost money on that message you showed us. . . on the the photograph. Even that crazy bitch Fisher must have lost money. It said 'BUY'. Look what happened: we got left for dead on the 50 point surge. The investigation you've started will see that. Why bother, George? Forget it. If you've any sense you'll come with me. I've still got money, though not as much as I thought I'd have."

This wasn't how I had expected it to go. In my mind, Eddie was the major villain of the piece, and I wanted him to stay that way, but in one day he'd saved my skin, told me something entirely contrary to what I had believed, and was offering me riches beyond his wildest dreams. The psychologists would say I was suffering from cognitive dissonance, I would say I was confused.

While I chewed all this over, Eddie had picked up his shirt and was pulling at it in disgust and annoyance. He dialled room service.

"Could you bring me a shirt. White cotton. Size, uh, 16. Moss Bros? Sure."

"You didn't have to kill him, you evil bastard."

I spat the words at him. My anger stopped me from being afraid. His nonchalant attitude to his own misdemeanours and the unravelling of my story stoked my temper. "I won't let you get away with it!"

"Kill who? Warren Graham isn't dead. Forget him. What's he to you? I swear I didn't know about them beating up on you. I wouldn't have let them do that. I care about you. Fisher, she's crazy . . . Look, George, no one's got killed. We just made some money, serious money. . . it was all about money, and now that I've got it I don't give a fuck about any of them."

He laughed at his last sentence like a man looking back, remembering with amusement a really good time that – if not had by all – was certainly had by him.

"Julian was murdered. You killed him," I shouted, wiping the crooked smile off his face.

He started to concentrate. "Julian was a friend of mine. He died. . .you know how he died," he protested, but I ignored his remonstration and raged back at him.

"Stop pretending, you hypocritical little shit. You broke into Julian's cottage, you took the stuff on Lifestyle, wiped his PC. You threatened Barnaby Page to stop us making the link between you, Julian and your tight-arsed mistress, Fisher. You gave him that message that brainwashed him senseless, just like it warped the minds of Rechter and all those dealers last week. Your serious money is seriously bad money, sick money, and your business stinks. You disgust me! I don't know why you brought me here, but you're not going to get away with this!"

Eddie came rapidly towards me but I jumped aside. He shouted, "Stop", "Listen," and "Wait a minute," but I ran hither and thither, shouting back, hurling accusations at him. It was a farce without the revolving doors. It reminded me of a holiday I once had in Portugal when I was seventeen and a Spanish golfer had chased me ardently around my holiday villa crying "We are like sheeps in the night". I just couldn't succumb to that sort of accent, but Eddie was bigger and uglier. The hotel room at The Tower gave me more room to move, but he cornered me eventually and forced me roughly on to the sofa, knocking over a small vase of pinks on the glass coffee table as he did so. It circled the table, tinkling delicately before gently dropping off into the deep, deep, pink pile of the carpet. Its little vibrating bell-like sound signalled time out. I held both my hands up.

"For Chrissake, Georgina, what do you think I'm gonna do to you?" Eddie muttered, breathing hard with exertion and frustration, drops of moisture running from his hair and mingling with the sweat on his forehead. There was a time when I would have looked up and longed for him to kiss me. He was still handsome but no longer attractive. I couldn't imagine him in faded jeans and a soft sweatshirt; I couldn't think of him with salt crusting on the hairs on his dark brown belly, or burying his toes in the soft sand as we watched the surf, or covering me with an old bomber-jacket when it started to rain. He lived in a world of mass-produced lifestyles and his strength was purchase power. His face was pale and his lips were greedy. To him, romance was cellophane-wrapped blood-red roses out of season, or even jet fresh strawberries and champagne in an airless room.

"I've already called Max. If I don't call him back he will call the police," I replied harshly.

Eddie ran his long fingers through his dark hair and walked away from me. He got as far as the seat opposite then turned angrily towards me.

"You ought to be more grateful. I've never ever laid a finger on you. . .and you know that. So help me, I don't intend to start now, but don't push it. Look, you stupid bitch, you know me, for Chrissake! Could I kill anyone? Think about it. The answer's no. I made a deal with him, and it went wrong. What could I do? Julian's death was an *accident*. Understand? The poor bastard killed himself fooling around like he did . . ."

I stared uncompromisingly at him, with a look of disgust and contempt on my face.

He continued, sneering back. "And what about this mistress thing. You jealous, or what? Who's supposed to be my mistress anyway? Kay? Oh boy, that'll be the day. I'd rather lay Madame Mao. I risked my ass in there for you today, or have you forgotten that?"

It was one of those moments which simply explode with an accumulation of resentments, old and new. I wanted to tear at him for a million humiliations since the very first one. The anger was all stored up in me and brought me screaming to my feet.

"I don't care who your mistresses are, you pathetic creep. And, oh yes, I do know you, I do bloody well know you. You! – you're a liar. You're physically and emotionally unable to tell the truth. You never could and never will. I don't believe anything you say or do. You a hero? Don't make me laugh! You got me out of there today for the benefit of Mr Eddie Powers, because he always comes first. You're lying about her, about the message and Julian. What have we come here for?"

We were both standing now, chins forward, trading abuse, accusations and insults. It was only a matter of time before Celia's name came up. Eddie laughed bitterly in my face.

"Oh, yeah. Now we're down to what really counts here. Who did I screw! Once, I tripped up. Once." His index finger was stabbing the air in front of my truculent face. "The woman came on to me every time we met. Your friend, my ass! Where did you find her? OK, I was stoned so I went with the flow. I said I was sorry a thousand times and, God knows, I meant it! You want to know the truth, I reckon she wanted *you* all the time. Think about it. But you, you never let me make it up to you. I called and called. You were as stubborn as a goddamned mule. OK, OK. My fault, my fault. It's over between us. *Mea culpa*. But we never talked about it, you just packed up your tent and left, baby. It got so bad that I just didn't care any more. I tried, but you wouldn't talk to me! Now, you want to join

172

the party? That's fine. You don't? That's your problem. I brought you here because a couple of jerks wanted to rip our heads off. End of story. You want to know about Julian, I'll tell you. But you'd better listen this time, and listen good."

I flipped open the top of a silver-plated cigarette box with my good hand, grasped a cigarette, stuck it in my mouth and lit it. Then I sank down into the corner of the grey settee, sending angry plumes of smoke out into the room. Eddie hated to see me smoke. He sat down irritably in a chair opposite me. Then the telephone rang. It was the management.

Our fight had disturbed the neighbours. Eddie apologised in a smooth, amiable "howdy folks" voice, ordered more food and champagne and asked where his shirt was. The latter would give the staff an opportunity to discreetly check whether I was still alive. I thought about my flat again. No one ever complained to the management there. There was no management. It was a closed-door democracy.

Eddie waited as room service set the coffee table with glasses and sandwiches. He gave the uniformed boy a large tip, and when the door clicked softly shut, he sat down.

"I didn't kill Julian. I don't know who killed him. I didn't know he had been killed. Shit, I thought he killed himself. That's the truth. I don't know what you mean about the message. I went into his place to get rid of some stuff, that's all. We didn't want Kirren Ventures traced through Lifestyle; that's all there was to it."

The cigarette was burning my throat. I realised I didn't really want to smoke it; it was just a substitute for what I really wanted: something to slow me down, something to take me out. Some pills perhaps. I wanted some pills, something to lift me up or slow me down, anything but this jumpy nerve-jangling tick-over. I took another drink instead.

Eddie explained what I knew already: how Julian had written the program and worked on it at the pizza house. They had planned to start up a business together to market it, but they hadn't been able to get the money. Eddie had started working at Broadwick's and had asked Kay Fisher for some contacts. She had wanted to see the program work. Eddie said she tried it on herself to help her stop biting her nails. It worked: she now had nice pearly fingernails. It was as simple as that. She arranged for the creation of a venture capital consortium called Kirren Ventures which was ostensibly established to fund Lifestyle.

"It was all kosher. Then she told me her plan. There were millions for the taking if we could use that program to give the market a little shove. Now it was work with her, or lose Lifestyle's three million dollars to begin with. All it had to do was move in the direction we wanted it to. Only a little. The market was climbing and climbing, any punts on a fall were cheap. We were into index options, and index futures; and currency. . .stuff that moved with markets not individual securities," Eddie explained.

"We knew the market was due for a little correction. It was just too pumped up. But we wanted to pre-empt it, time it so the drop didn't take us by surprise. It was like opening a cupboard door stuffed with tin cans. Hell, it was. . .well, shit, did it slide? We never expected that slide! Shit!" Eddie was shaking his head in disbelief and the sort of sublime enjoyment that comes with a white-knuckle ride.

"Getting in on Rechter's system was easy. We intercepted a line and made him download the program while logging on to some remote database. After that, every time he switched on his PC, that little program loaded up. Julian set the thing up at the Stock Exchange so that anyone who saw TOPIC saw the message.

"But he started to get really nervous about the whole thing. He wanted out. I told him no one could trace him at Lifestyle; we'd even get him headhunted to cover it up. But he was nervous, and Kay thought he could screw up the whole project. She wanted to kick ass."

"So you changed the message at the pizza house?" I said coolly.

"Yeah. Well, no. . .not me personally, but yes we wanted him to forget."

"Forget the key?"

"Sure, yes. You found that?" Eddie was impressed.

"Didn't you know?" I replied suspiciously and explained how Warren and I had got into the pizza house computer.

Eddie's face was grim and expressionless while he continued.

"That was the codename to the project Key – like to the city. And it worked. He was getting pretty vague about it all . . .but we needn't have bothered. The poor sap died anyway."

Eddie voice choked a little. I looked hard at him. The man was genuinely upset about Julian's death, and I now believed that he didn't know what had really happened.

"Did you know about Julian's, er, hobby?" I said dully.

Eddie nodded miserably.

"Do you know how he died?" I asked, not knowing if the rising emotion in me would erupt in crazy laughter or bitter rage.

Eddie nodded. "He suffocated in that stupid rubber mask of his," he replied.

"That's right, sweetie, that's right. Because he forgot his key. Geddit? Big joke. He forgot his damned key! He died because he left the key to his bloody handcuffs in a drawer. Can you imagine! My God! He didn't just forget your damned project, you stupid bastards. He forgot a real key. I'm surprised he was able to get in and out of his house, or start his car. . . oh, Jesus! I'm going to go insane!"

I held my throat to stop myself screaming with the crazy horror of it.

Eddie's face was still and white. It was as if a bomb had gone off within the confines of his brain.

"Honest to God, I didn't know, George, believe me. It's so off the wall. . . how was I to know? I didn't know. He was my friend, believe me, George," he muttered anxiously, reaching for me in rising panic but I pushed his hand away.

"You stupid bastards!" I shrieked, hurling the glass I held at the wall.

We sat for a long time in crushed silence. Then I got up, walked to the telephone and dialled out.

"Max, it's OK. See you Monday. Yeah, it's really OK."

I replaced the receiver. I could hear that reggae beat. Diddy-dum, diddy-dum, diddy-diddy-diddy-dum. It seemed to throb in a vein in my head. I wished it would stop.

"It was an accident, please, Georgina, it was a mistake. We were going to make it together. Please believe me."

Eddie pleaded again in a low anxious voice as I sat down wearily next to him.

"That's as may be, Eddie dearest. Have some more champagne, do, and give me an explanation. I might just believe my poor cousin's farcical death was an unfortunate mistake. But if you didn't know that that program had killed Julian, who did? Because whoever did, they wiped the program from the pizza house, wrecked my flat with a vengeance, and half killed me in a car park. Fisher knew, didn't she? Now, don't tell me she didn't know! You'd better tell me what you know."

There was no time for Eddie to reply. Instead, there was a hard rap at the door and one word.

"Police."

CHAPTER THIRTEEN

WE SPED THROUGH THE DRIZZLY streets of London towards Bishopsgate. The electric paintbox of fuzzy city lights winked through the raindrops that streaked across the solid windows of the police car. Eddie sat sheepishly in silence beside me, and he said nothing even as they led me down a fluorescent lamp-lit corridor to a small dust-coloured room with no windows. It smelled much used, like an ancient waiting room, tainted and rancid with the reeking ash of a thousand desperate cigarettes and stale body odour.

I sat for an hour alone in there, wondering why nothing was falling into place. I should have been the star witness, I was a victim, but I was sitting there accused.

"Georgina Powers? I have a warrant for your arrest." Two squat plainclothes policemen and a large overweight house detective blocked the door as Eddie, who had the decency to look surprised at least, stood back.

Foreboding replaced anger as we cruised into the yard of the police station. Whom the gods are undecided about destroying, they first make mad, and then a little madder, and so on. As I sat, leaning forward over the square Formica table, my head resting on my folded arms, I knew they were getting pretty close to that.

My first visitor was a doctor. I could hear his breath whistling through his nostrils and smell his last cigarette as he shone a pen-light in my eyes. He carefully unrolled my bandage to check my wound, dressed it again and left without a word. The bandage was too tight and blood began to accumulate uncomfortably in my fingertips. My head started to ache again, and my stomach felt empty enough to be pressing on my backbone.

My Swatch ticked like a kitchen timer, cranking out the

minutes as they passed. I tried to think calmly, reasonably, but my animated imagination was winning, and I was tiring fast. Why hadn't they offered me a solicitor? No, that was in US detective series. Here, you had to ask for one, I thought, cursing the fact that I hadn't the useful experience of being in more trouble before. Hope glowed like a revitalised ember as I determined to demand a telephone call, only to be snuffed out by the realisation that I only knew one solicitor and he was probably tucked up in bed after a hard day coping with my divorce.

Max. I had to call Max. But Max. . .? A creepy feeling of doubt began to worm around inside of me. I had told him I was at the hotel. No one else knew. Could I trust Max? He knew everything, almost, but what was he up to?

The door opened and a large straw-haired man wearing steely glasses entered the room. A trim policewoman followed, carrying two teas in thick green china cups and saucers. She set them down with a dull tinkle, while my visitor pulled up the second of three wooden chairs in the room and sat down heavily opposite me. There were dark sweatmarks on his white shirt, and large ginger freckles speckled his ample arms, which bulged from his white rolled-up shirtsleeves. He had a head like a bucket but his mouth was sweet, like a cupid's bow.

"Detective Inspector Robert Falk," he said quietly, opening quickly a black vinyl folder and wrapping his banana fingers around a black pen. With a delicate pop, he pulled the top off and placed it carefully on the other end. The long night's work began with questions to confirm existing details of my name, address and occupation.

"Right name, right job, wrong address," I replied sanguinely. Falk looked at his notes and up again with a quizzical look.

"It's not my address," I repeated firmly. "I live in the flat directly downstairs."

Falk flicked his eyes over a peppermint-green-lined sheaf of computer printout.

"The housing association lists you as the sole occupant, Mrs Powers."

"Well, I'm not. I live downstairs, on the floor below. Number 501. You know, like the Levis."

Falk jotted this down in a small neat hand, his progress across the page reminiscent of an elephant tiptoeing across a window ledge. He checked the printout again.

"501 is listed as vacant, awaiting refurbishment."

"I should think so. It was broken into on Tuesday night and comprehensively demolished. Check it."

"Who do you say is the occupant of 601?" Falk sighed, unconvinced.

"Warren Graham"

"Occupation?"

"Taxi driver."

"Friend?"

"Yes."

Falk browsed though the printout again.

"He's not listed."

"He's lived there for years. I know," I insisted, my voice creeping up an octave.

"Our information is that 501 has been empty for two years, and that you have been the sole occupant of 601 for five years." Falk was staring levelly at me, his pale bespectactled eyes fixed and cool, like pebbles in a pool.

"Look what is this about?" I demanded, wondering how I was going to explain that Warren had probably fixed it, in his own special way, for me to take over the flat so no questions would be asked.

Falk's reply was so close, it caught me off guard.

"Hacking, Mrs Powers. We have reason to believe that you have been using your personal computer in flat 601 to make unauthorised accesses to a private minicomputer elsewhere."

I blushed hotly. "That's ridiculous!" I scoffed unconvincingly, feeling the heat of my cheeks condemn me.

"You are a computer journalist, are you not? So it's not impossible," Falk offered, smiling faintly.

"I write about computers and the industry, Detective, otherwise I know bugger all about them. You drive a car, don't you? When did you last fix one? When was I supposed to have hacked in anyway?"

"The last recorded entry was at 8.00 am, this morning. . ." Falk glanced down at his thick digital watch, "I beg your pardon, yesterday morning."

"I was in hospital. Check it. You can also check what your night duty at Bow was up to on Tuesday night. With any luck, their records aren't computerised and in some brown paper folder will be a badly-typed report of a call-out to my flat: 501. I repeat: number 501." I was gaining confidence now that I had an alibi, but I knew I had to be cautious. Warren must have been busy that day and I wanted to know why.

Falk noted what I said and laid his pen down. Then, he leaned his bulk forward until I could smell him, hot and warm under his shirt, like baked bread, his huge head wobbling with the momentum. He pressed a pudgy index finger onto the steel frame of his glasses and slid them back up on the broad bridge of the fleshy nose. The action drew my attention to a mole, fixed and round, like a well-placed beauty spot below his eye, anchored to his well-hidden cheekbone.

"This is all very strange, isn't it, Mrs Powers," he said companionably.

I didn't answer but leaned back away from him, to get some space, to get some air. The room was muggy and my eyes felt damp and sticky. The damned Swatch was thundering like a heart throbbing on my sleeve.

"Where is my husband?"

"He answered our questions to our satisfaction and he has been allowed to leave," Falk replied with equanimity, his huge arms folded across the table.

"Nice," I said sourly. The irony of it. Instead of Eddie or Fisher, I was incarcerated here in a stinking four-by-six broomcupboard in the early hours of Saturday morning with a bloated stormtrooper from the Met and City Company Fraud Unit, Computer Section. It was not a heavily funded, nor highly thought of little band among its peers, but that was of little comfort to me then.

"Look, I'd like to make a telephone call, if you don't mind," I said, and Falk drew back.

"Of course, come with me."

"Max, I'm at Bishopsgate nick!" I whispered desperately down the line.

"Good, they found you."

His words hit me like a well-aimed brick.

"What the hell did you do that for?" I exploded, barely in control.

"I was concerned, so I had to call the police. Nick followed you and came back saying that he'd seen you being dragged down a corridor, chased by some thugs with a gun. He got pictures, so of course we reported it."

"I said I was OK." My voice was cracking with the strain of wanting to shout but only just being able to breathe.

"I thought you were probably being held against your will," he replied, his self-satisfaction infuriating me.

"So why am I stuck in here facing a frigging charge?"

"I don't know and don't swear at me!" Max growled through gritted teeth, but with ear-blasting voice projection.

There are times when life in general is a real bitch. There I was battered, bruised, cut and incarcerated without the tiniest clue as to who the hell was on my side. There was one treat in store: I was going to get to see Max in a completely different environment. He and Nick were going to come to the station.

"I don't like to sound ungrateful but could you bring a solicitor," I whispered.

"Oh, ye of little faith," Max replied unfeelingly.

I carefully replaced the receiver in its cradle and held my hands over my face. Falk padded down the corridor towards me and gently escorted me back to the sweat box.

"Look, I'm very tired," I said miserably as we took our seats. "Couldn't we continue this discussion at another time? I am not your hacker. I have an alibi."

Falk shook his huge head. "Someone will be joining us

shortly," he said, opening up his folder again and closing his finger around the pen top. I waited for the short quick sound of released suction. "I've ordered more tea," he added politely.

Tea arrived ten minutes later, followed by a tall, unprepossessing gentleman in a blue pin-striped suit. He wore a red tie sporting some sort of emblem, and a blue-striped shirt with an unfashionable white contrasting collar. Flakes of scurf rode the waves of his greasy grey hair. He sat down silently in the third chair, pulling it slightly behind Falk, and placed a battered brown briefcase on the floor by his black-nosed feet.

"The man with no name?" I remarked, hoisting an insolent eyebrow in the newcomer's direction.

Falk twisted uncomfortably in his chair in an effort to turn around, but managed only to swivel his eyeballs.

"This is Douglas Macnemie of the Stock Exchange."

"Hello," I said, smiling.

Macnemie moved not an atrophied muscle, so I decided to ignore him and concentrate on the perspiring Falk.

"The minicomputer which was accessed was one of those which operate the Stock Exchange's TOPIC system," Falk began. "The call was traced to a personal computer in your flat in Bow. Can you explain this, Mrs Powers?"

"It's not my flat and I have no explanation," I replied tautly. "So what was supposed to have happened?"

"We have no information at this point, Mrs Powers," Falk replied.

I looked back at him, barely suppressing a smile. "So what's the crime? You can't hold me here. You've got nothing. Good night, Detective Inspector Falk . . . Mr Macnemie. I'm amazed you have a warrant at all," I said, rising to go.

Falk leaned forward on his huge arms and cracked his submerged knuckles.

"Sit down, Mrs Powers," he said coolly. "This flat which you claim is not yours has been rented by you for the past five years. The flat which you say is yours has been derelict for two years. You stated that flat 601 is in fact rented to

Warren Graham, a taxi driver. There is no Warren Graham listed in the records of the Hackney Carriage Office. Nor at the DVLC. I take it that if he exists, he is male? The report of the search of your flat. . . of flat 601. . . states that it is furnished in an overtly feminine way. There are women's clothes and shoes in the wardrobe, female underwear in the drawers. Is he a transvestite?"

"No. . . not to my knowledge," I said, suddenly reminded of Julian's transmogrified boy-scout persona.

"The telephone number is in your name, and finally there is this photograph. . . It was on your dressing table."

Falk hauled up a labelled plastic bag containing on old photograph in a new gilt frame. The slit had been repaired, but it was the picture of Julian, Anne, Richard, the dog and I all standing together on a sunny clifftop long, long ago.

This was Warren's little gift: a new flat, and new clothes for my new start in his flat. If only he knew how things were turning out. I wanted to kill him for his kindness.

"This document was there, too," Falk continued, opening an envelope. I unfolded the thin computer-printed paper. It contained details of my account with Broadwick & Klein. I scanned the bottom line and found the figure £75,000. It purported to represent the gains I had made on writing calls on index options over the past account.

I stared at Falk for further clues. None were forthcoming.

"This is owed to me?" I croaked in astonishment.

Falk nodded, his chins puffing out frog-like with each downward push. The room felt as if it was two fathoms down. Macnemie's crushing silence and Falk's scratching pen on paper joined with my Swatch in a depressing conspiracy to discomfort equal to the ancient practice of Chinese water torture.

Eddie had said that he'd lost money on that message. Of course he had; it was the wrong message. Eddie's message was "SELL". Warren had changed it. He must have done. Warren had hacked in and changed it. He'd shafted them with a fifty point surge. He'd got there before me and hadn't told me. He'd been caught trying to wipe it out, but not before making me some money, and probably a load for himself. He'd wanted to set me up, so sweetly, to help me get my life straight, with money, with things. He couldn't not interfere in my life. My life wasn't good enough for him. He wanted something better for me. Well, I'd been set up all right, like a sitting painted frigging decoy duck.

"This mysterious Warren Graham, who exists not in the eyes of the Hackney Carriage Office, nor the DVLC, nor in any of our records here – where is he now, Mrs Powers?"

"I don't know."

"When did you last see him?"

"Thursday night."

"When did you last speak to him?"

"Friday morning."

"Could you give us a description?"

"I could, I might."

"Do you think he hacked this computer, Mrs Powers?" he ventured with outrageous opportunism, spreading his banana fingers on the table and wetting his erubescent lips. I rubbed my damaged aching hand and lifted its purple fingertips to my dry lips. Falk ought to have been making the same connections that I was. Someone who could hack into TOPIC could wipe himself off any database, if he chose, could change a silly list of tenants in a housing association computer, could just disappear. Erase himself.

"I really cannot answer that," I said dully. "In fact, I'm not answering any more questions. I have an alibi. I was in hospital on Friday morning. My own flat was vandalised on Tuesday night. I paid my rent by cheque. Anyone could have opened that account for me. I'm just working on a story, that's all. In fact, it should be on record that my paper, *Technology Week*, on information that I provided, contacted the Stock Exchange on Friday afternoon warning it to check its system. It maintained its system was clear. So hack or no hack, what's the problem?"

I didn't get an answer.

Max, Nick and the solicitor arrived at 2.00 am. I hadn't tried to sleep. Instead I sat on the hard bench in my cell, contemplating the dilemma in which I found myself. It had to be Warren who had made that access. His smart-assed act of sentimentality had delivered me into the hands of my enemies. Now Eddie, Fisher and the others had a head start, and I couldn't rescue myself without dropping Warren in it. I still wanted to kill him. Why couldn't he have just handed over his rent book like everyone else did, or couldn't he trust me to keep up the payments on the flat? Had I given that good an impression of a girl on the slide?

There was something on my side. The police hadn't caught anyone red-handed. Anyone could have made that call from my flat. They had the same problem that I had encountered in all of this; when they broke down the door no one was holding the smoking gun.

"Thanks, guys," I said as Nick sheepishly pushed Max into the cell, followed by a short, baggy-suited man whom I took to be the solicitor.

"Calm yourself, Georgina," Max said irritably in an attempt to pre-empt any withering remark that I had simmering. He held up his pale hands like a latter-day paraclete. I hate people who say calm yourself when you are calm and have every reason not to be.

"I told you I was OK," I said calmly.

"Look, I thought someone had made you say that, especially after what Nick here reported," Max replied a little huffily. I shot Nick a curious look, and Max hurriedly introduced the solicitor, Charles Branagh.

"You really shouldn't have said anything at all, Georgina. They insist they have enough information to keep you for at least forty-eight hours," Branagh said, making it sound as if my predicament was my fault.

I closed my eyes, hoping that when I opened them I would be asleep.

"The access charge is minor, of course, and they cannot make that stick. It's the conspiracy charge that is worrying. They think they have you on fraud."

"I'll show them my overdraft," I said, starting to laugh to cover my nervousness.

"Well, Georgina, you might have an overdraft but you're due £75,000 out of Broadwick & Klein which you have yet to explain," Branagh replied

"I can't explain it. I've been set up."

"Look, Georgina. Let's give the police the information we have now, right from the beginning. Give them the names you have at Broadwick's," said Max, with avuncular severity. "You. . .we have a great story."

It wasn't how I'd wanted it to work out, not at all, but I wasn't going to say anything yet. Branagh did his bit, and I was sitting in Max's comfortable armchair by 3.00 am. Max's housekeeper Madelaine chided and ordered him to bed. She was a petite, round-faced, dark-haired Malaysian of about thirty-five, and when she had settled Max in his room, she came back and waited.

"You need sleep. Nick, you too – in here. Pull out the bed, and I will bring the sleeping-bag," she said, placing her tiny golden hand on my shoulder when she had finished. The nails of her little fingers and thumbs were incredibly long, curved and finely manicured, the others were cut short. Four nails kept face, telling the world that she didn't serve all the time.

"Not yet. I need a drink, Madelaine," I said wearily, and she went immediately to fetch Nick and me two large tumblers of Max's Old Bushmills.

Nick sat opposite me in another deep armchair. He smiled and offered me a cigarette, which I refused with a shake of my head. "I haven't got anything stronger," he added, but I didn't respond except to stare flatly at him. He looked disappointed. He lit himself a cigarette, inhaled deeply, and blew the smoke out through the gap in his teeth. Then he told me what had happened after I had left the office.

He had seen me take a cab, and had followed me on his bike to Kleintel's. Posing as my photographer, he told the receptionist he was running late, so the second security guard had sent him on up to the seventh floor, assuming he would encounter the first security guard and be taken to wherever I was. The guard was waiting to enter the lift as Nick arrived at the seventh floor, but had simply pointed him in the direction of the conference room.

"Once the guard had gone, I came back and waited at the end of the corridor. I saw your husband get out of the lift so I started to walk towards it, hoping he'd assume I was a messenger. That worked, so I waited again, out of sight. When I heard a scuffle, I peeped down the corridor and saw you being dragged into the Gents. I got a shot off then," Nick continued, getting up and confidently pouring us both another round of Max's whiskey. I must have looked cautious about drinking it, so Nick gently pressed my good hand around the glass and patted it warmly.

"There is a lot more where that came from, I can assure you. I'll buy the old bastard another one if you like. Just relax, will you?"

He sat down and continued while I leaned back in my chair and sipped.

"Well, I started to go after you, when these two guys ran from the room with Fisher rapping out instructions. I started to take some more shots while I ran backwards to the lift. I felt pretty safe because I figured no one was going to take a swing at me while I was rigged out in full motorcycle kit. Well, then I saw the gun, and just about shit myself. I haven't seen one of those since. . .well never mind that.

"Anyway, a door banged and Fisher told them to leave me and follow you. They all turned and legged it round the corner and down the corridor. Fisher went back into that room and started to call someone – security – so I ran back to the stairs by the lift and got down to reception. I walked straight through."

"No one bothered you?" I asked, a little surprised.

"No, too busy with you two, I suppose. I waited out on the street. I sat on the bike just a little down the way. I figured someone would come out and I could take some more shots. It was dark, but the lights of the reception area lit the street, which was pretty well-lit anyway. I didn't think there would be a problem."

"Who did you snap?" I asked, draining my glass. The fire of the whiskey warmed my throat and chest and misted my eyes.

"You and your husband. . .sorry, ex-husband."

"Not quite."

"Then the Japanese guy and his friend – and finally Ms Fisher. That one is a bit unclear."

"Can I see them?" I said.

"Sure."

Nick got up and fetched over a brown paper envelope, which he handed to me. I opened it and gazed at the contents in silence. Fisher was dressed in a smart trenchcoat; Nick had caught her, trim black briefcase in hand, stepping into a taxi. The outside shots were good, though Fisher was partially obscured by the taxi in one of them.

The pictures of Eddie and me shocked me. We looked harassed, of course, but his arm was around my shoulder, protecting me, holding me. It was all wrong. I held up the photographs to peer at them closely in the subdued lighting of Max's sitting-room.

"You've given these to Falk, I suppose," I muttered.

"Branagh suggested we did. At least it gives the police something else to do. . .look, Georgina, I'm sorry. . .I was trying to help."

"I don't need your help. I'm sick of people helping me. When people help me I feel the noose tightening around my neck. You should have kept your nose out of my business." I leaned back with my eyes closed so I wouldn't have to see his face.

His voice was emotional. "But it is my business. My nose is in it, rubbed in it. They came to my flat and tore it apart, all my work destroyed. . .What about your flat? What about you? One night I find you running scared, another morning you're beaten and cut. You can't do this on your own, George."

I opened my eyes as Madelaine entered the room carrying Nick's bedclothes. I got up and let the photographs drop onto the coffee table by the empty tumblers.

"Look, sorry. . .I'm just out of it at the moment. I'm going downstairs to check something. I'll see you tomorrow."

It was disquieting to sit at Max's unkempt desk and tap my password on his keyboard. It was like the first time I had driven my father's car, an honour I had enjoyed but once, while he sat tensely in the passenger's seat keeping my speed to twenty-five miles an hour through sheer willpower. I hadn't been able to bring myself to so much as pull the seat forward, for fear of upsetting the great paternal order of things. Of course, there was no seat at Max's desk, just a dead console emanating authority. I was at the hallowed place where Max's ashtray, his notebook, his diary, his directories, his terminal dwelt.

I pulled up a chair and tentatively touched the keyboard. The dusty screen came alive. If I had known Max's password, I wonder what I would have seen? What secrets did he store away in this jewel box? I tapped in my own code and got through to the bulletin board. There was no message from Warren. There was nothing in my mail-box either. Where was he, I thought, baffled and impatient at the impenetrable mystery of his disappearance. Had he taken the money and run?

I gazed from the light of Max's desk across the dark office. The sound of dustcarts clearing the wet streets rumbled outside. Some traffic still slushed by, but the rain had stopped. Someone was singing "Danny Boy". I began to pick nonchalantly at my bandage, unravelling and unwinding the creamy crepe until it stretched down to the floor and I could peel away the crusty gauze that covered the slice in my hand. The cut was a straight dark line bonded tight with blood and brown thread, which stuck out on either side like nascent insect legs. My meshed metacarpals expanded and relaxed. Circulation tingled in my fingertips and drained away as I lifted my hand up to my face, my pale fingers a ghastly white against the sore red relief running the length of my palm.

"Everything you tried to do right, you did wrong, Warren," I whispered, sitting as still as a mummy trailing ancient bandages on the floor, gazing out across a gothic technological wasteland of wires and boxed cathode-ray tubes. I felt like a creature awoken out of its time, watching some preternatural sunrise shine through the grimy windows of a strange room in an alien city.

The key to this bungled Machiavellian plot was in my head. I'd missed something. With my left hand, I tapped J. Kirren on the dead keyboard, and then J/Kirren, and then repeated the finger exercise. Rubber. Nothing.

"Mrs Powers. . ." a soft voice called from the doorway.

"Come up now."

It was Madelaine. She walked over and, taking the bandage, rolled it up to begin dressing my hand again. "I have made tea, Mrs Powers. Drink some before you sleep."

"Madelaine, thank you, and it's Georgina, please," I replied, a little embarrassed at her kindness.

"I can't sleep, Madelaine," I said later as I sat on the bed in Max's guest-room, sipping at the pale bitter infusion she had prepared. "I cannot stop thinking. I feel like a hamster in a wheel."

"Lie down. Don't try. Just sleep. You will see, dreams wash thought. Tomorrow. . . today. . . you will have an answer."

She was right.

CHAPTER FOURTEEN

M ADELAINE WOKE ME AT TWO in the afternoon. There was a phone call from Eddie.

"You OK?" he said, as I sat bleary-eyed and dry-mouthed in the armchair I had sat in last night.

"Sure," I murmured cynically, leaning forward a little to look at Nick's photographs which lay in a neat pile on the edge of the table. The empty tumblers had been cleared away and the wooden coffee table shone brightly in the afternoon light. "Sure, I'm fine. How are you? What's more to the point, where are you? Still in this country?"

There was a silence that extended longer than the numerous interspersed stutters on the line. The connection was bad. I wasn't sure whether Eddie was calling from a cellular telephone or via satellite from some safe haven close to his freshly-laundered money. The line broke up, then his voice returned.

"Never mind where I am. What happened last night?"

"They think I hacked into TOPIC. I've also got an unwelcome £75,000 winging its way to my bank account. They'd like me to explain."

"Let's meet."

"Where?"

"South Bank."

"Pick somewhere warm and cosy, why don't you?"

"By Old Smokey. Half an hour."

My husband was untrustworthy but I had to admire his intestinal fortitude. I frowned and cautiously replaced the receiver. Then I nonchalantly flicked over the black and white photographs. They were amusing in a way, theatrical shots of the cast for the playhouse foyer. The bungling goons were grimacing like South American desperados, Eddie and I looked harassed and dishevelled, his big arms enfolding my narrow shoulders while we hurried up the street. Fisher, grim and white-faced, was bending into the cab, and the driver was twisting his dark head around towards her. I looked again at the grainy blow-up but this time not at Fisher – instead at the driver. I was sure I recognised him. I looked hard. The nose, the ears, the neck, the new haircut, the leather jacket – it was Warren all right. He'd got her; the crazy idiot had got her.

Nick came into the room with two mugs of hot tea. I grabbed one with a quick "Thank you" and rushed to my own room to dress.

"Where are you going?" he inquired as I hurried into the front room again, picked up the photograph of Warren and shoved it into my bag.

"May I? Good. I'm going to meet someone. You can follow me, if you like."

Nick shrugged his broad shoulders like a lazy bear. He scratched the dark stubble on his chin.

"Are you being funny?"

"No, I mean it. At least I'll know where you are, and you could keep an eye on things."

He didn't answer and I grabbed my jacket.

"Why don't you leave this to the police now?" he said, sipping at his tea

"Don't be boring, dear. This is my job."

He sat for a few seconds and thought about it.

"Bring camera?"

"Well. . . you never know, do you?" I said with a brief laugh.

"What about Max?"

"We'll catch him later. Now come on!"

We made our own separate ways to the Royal Festival Hall. The clouds had cleared and the sun was bright, but the wind still whistled around the huge bare concrete building blocks and their bleak interconnecting walkways. Variegated neon boxes glowed in alternate geometric colour above the NFT and the Hayward. Huge, lonely, grey, globular posts pointed circituous routes to the sheer slabs that hid cinemas, theatres, galleries and concert halls.

Coming to an event here was rather like approaching a refrigerator; you have to expect all the goodies to be on the inside.

I stepped up the stairs and walked around the huge, square, glass frontage of the Festival Hall, the breeze from the Thames catching at my jeans and jacket, whipping back my hair.

Eddie stood by the knotty sculpture waiting for me.

"He's still got it," he said.

I looked up at the modern depiction of the cellist who looked for all the world like an aged emaciated dosser busking outside Waterloo Station. Someone had stuck an old cigarette butt in his open mouth when we'd seen it last. It was still there, the same one, unless some wag had renewed it – probably Eddie, for manipulative reasons.

"Yes," I murmured, knowing he wanted me to reminisce, to share again this fragment of our past. We'd discovered it together one evening years ago. Eddie had sung an awful Dick van Dyke cockney version of "Any Old Iron" in front of it, and I'd pretended not to know him.

"He still looks down on his luck, eh?" Eddie said, looking away from me and the crusty old musician, turning his square chin to the river.

"What about you?" I retorted, dragging myself back to the present.

"Me?" he smiled back at me. "Me? Not me. I've made more money than you can imagine, babe, if that surge didn't wipe us out. Kirren Ventures, coffers should be overflowing if Fisher did her bit. She comes away a rich lady. Too bad, eh?"

We walked together towards the river and leaned on the barrier. I saw Nick lighting a cigarette about fifty feet away. I knew I wouldn't need him now, not if Eddie was alone and hadn't been followed.

"Look, I know who hacked into TOPIC and so do you. What's the story, Eddie? Did Warren Graham try to cut you all out, and cut him and me in? Look at this."

Eddie looked grimly at the photograph of Fisher getting into the cab. The wind was tugging at his dark hair, pulling it back from his pale forehead. The lemon smell of his after-shave blew into my face. He handed me back the photograph and thrust his hands in his beige Burberry pockets.

"What do you see?" I demanded "C'mon."

"Fisher."

"And?"

"Warren Graham."

"What do you know about him?"

"He probably lost me a fortune."

"By how much."

"Well, I don't know. . . yet. We had forty before he changed the message – that's if Fisher, the rocket scientist, kept her head. He screwed me up. Hell, what the fuck, I can live on ten million, for Chrissake."

"You mean he threw your bets out of synch?"

"Yes. I was caught dead by the surge while I was doing a little private dealing, and what made matters worse I didn't believe the run would hold. I thought the message still said "SELL". Look, I wanted to tell you last night but we were . . . interrupted. I saw that "BUY" message on that photograph you sent up and it hit me right between the eyes."

The wind was singing around the arched roof of the Royal Festival hall, and a discarded Coca-Cola can clattered by on its lonely way to the stairs. Eddie turned sharply towards me.

"If I was caught dead, so should she have been. . . or was she? She could have lost the lot, but I don't think so. Know what I mean?"

"I think so. You mean Fisher knew about the message, and if so Warren did it for her. They did it together. Was I set up, too?"

Eddie brought out a packet of sugar-free gum, un-wrapped one and stuck it in his mouth. He offered me some, but I didn't think my jaw would stand it. I waited while he considered his position.

"That Graham. . . what's he to you?" he said, chewing quickly. He always hated to come right out with something; there had to be a weighing-up of outcomes, an assessment of what was in it for him.

"Nothing," I replied, less than honestly. My hand began to ache and I looked out over the river running fast and brown under the grey bridges and the blue, cloud-scudded sky. Nick had his back to it, his hair was blowing over his face, his face and hands looked cold. I knew Eddie was going to tell me something that I didn't want to hear.

"He's a renegade, you know that? We paid him, Fisher and me. We had to use him to hack Rechter's machine for us. We paid him."

I couldn't look at Eddie. I couldn't let him see the tears that had glazed my eyes. I looked across at the bulbous dome of St Pauls against a block-graph backdrop of grey towers and busy insect-like cranes, and I thought of Warren in his new suit and gold watch, flicking notes from his gold money-clip.

"And Julian?" I said slowly, choking a little.

"Yeah. He set up the pizza house message, too. Warren Graham did it. I couldn't do that. I did the cottage, but he set up the message. Oh. . for Chrissake, George, it was an accident."

I'd known it before he had said it. The sound of a London taxi is so distinct. I heard one now, passing by under the railway arches, and I had heard it that night in the car park. It came rumbling back with my memory. He hadn't just set up the message for Julian; he'd betrayed me over and over again. He couldn't kill me, though. He couldn't join Fisher's boys. There had been a limit to what he would do for money and freedom. She had wanted me dead, with £75,000 in the bank, with a trace to a hacker's computer, in a flat in my name. He had helped set me up, but he couldn't quite finish the job.

I gazed ruefully at the photograph. I had thought he had pulled off a great trick for our revenge on them. I thought he had played the white knight just one more time, but Madelaine was right – my dreams had washed my thoughts. The password to the pizza house kept coming back to me. The key was in my head.

Warren had tapped my cousin's name straight into the computer that night at the cottage. He had tapped in

J.Kirren first, then J/Kirren, and then the password, after a decent lapse of time and effort. There was something wrong then, but I hadn't picked it up. How could he have known Julian's name? I hadn't told him Julian's name. He had faked the hack. That's why he had looked so unhappy when I told him our target was Pull-Up For Pizza. If he had given up, walked away, I would have known something was wrong from the start. My flat, Nick's flat, the program wiped out; it was Warren all along, telling her how close I was getting, trying to scare me off.

"It was an accident, George," Eddie pleaded gently. "We didn't want that message to kill him, believe me. The rest is . . . well, nothing to do with me."

"You mean my flat, Nick's flat. . . This!" I snapped holding up my arm. "Of course, it was something to do with you. You started all this. You helped Fisher."

"I told you, she's crazy, OTT. I didn't know about it. It might mean nothing to you, but you're still my wife, you mean something to me. . . and shit, even if you didn't, I couldn't hurt you . . . Fuck, I couldn't kill anyone. Fisher wanted you to stop nosing around, but I didn't think it had got that serious. I can explain that too. . . if you like."

"Oh, do me a favour," I stammered, hot tears rolling freely down my nose. I began to sob with rage and despair. Eddie took hold of me, smoothing his useless hands over my shoulders in an uncomfortable attempt to soothe me.

"Um. . . tell me something. Do you sleep with the guy?" he asked at last, when my open grief had part subsided, pressing a monogrammed white handkerchief into my hand.

"No. . .it was awful close though," I sniffed, dabbing my eyes and nose.

"Um. . .good," he replied. I peered curiously at his face from behind the damp cloth.

"Why?"

"'Cos Fisher does. I know you thought it was me and her, but she's always preferred ethnic minorities, and she really is in to this one. You know, I'm feeling kind of exposed right now."

He wasn't talking about the weather. I felt the same way. I'd hauled in the Trojan Horse – Warren's flat, the £75,000 . . . and he'd probably set up other things that would make me look like the Stock Exchange hacker. I began to worry about my bank account records. If Eddie hadn't know about the message, then Warren and Fisher had double-crossed him, and Eddie was on the way out.

"Who is Kirren Ventures – effectively?" I asked.

"Julian, Kay, me."

"Julian's dead."

"Kay. . . me. . ." Eddie's voice trailed pensively away.

"Yes, you're right. You are very exposed, aren't you? What if they want it all to themselves? They've set us up but they must know that I, at least, would tell the authorities. And the authorities on both sides of the Atlantic, they must know about the program. Where are you going to hide, Eddie?"

Eddie kissed his hand, placed it gently on my lips, and laughed wryly.

"I've something to trade, babe."

"What have you got to trade?" I asked suspiciously.

"The status quo," he replied.

He was right. No one was going to be in that great a hurry to reveal that the great electronic global financial marketplace had even been penetrated, let alone undermined. In a way, it was worse news than if the defence systems of the Western alliance had been breached. Such an incident is part of the global game of advantage played by armed protagonists, after all. Even terrorists, our own and other people's, wouldn't, couldn't, press their advantage home to achieve ultimate irrevocable nemesis. For in this nuclear world, the end means there are no prizes left for anyone. But give them a way to punch a hole in the prize itself – capitalism – and they will have circumvented the nuclear fortress and achieved their aim without a shot fired in anger. Eddie would have to be very careful how he traded.

"Eddie, we all know too much, as they say. We've got

197

Fisher and Warren to worry about, and we've got our own side to worry about, too," I warned.

"Yeah, you're right, and if the lady of the Grand Old Opry gets to sing, you can bet she'll want to sing first, and alone."

We stood in silent contemplation for a while, looking down at the sullen swollen river running fast, confidently hemmed by the broad square buildings of city. I counted the taxis that crossed the span of Waterloo Bridge, and wondered about Warren. Was everything he had said to me a lie? I didn't think so, no more than everything Eddie had said was. I understood that now. There were no rules that you could lay down for surviving and understanding. The only rule was adapt. I'd had the experience, but I had missed the meaning – until then. I hoped I'd learned something.

"You're a crook, Eddie, but I think I can trust you on this one," I said and scooping the strands of windswept hair from my face, I told him what I thought we could do.

The wind whipped at Eddie's coat as he strode quickly away from me towards Waterloo. When he got to the stairs, he stopped and turned, shouting back at me.

"Hey, listen. You still want a divorce?"

"Of course I do," I called back. "You don't expect me to wait for you while you finish your sentence, do you?"

He laughed and pointed his finger like a gun at me.

"OK, OK. Tell your friend to come over now," he replied, and disappeared down the stairwell.

I stood buffeted by the wind, clutching a piece of paper and the photograph in my hand. On the paper, Eddie had scrawled his number and an address where he would be, and another where Fisher would almost certainly be. He wasn't sure about Warren, and neither was I.

"I don't think you should meet her," Nick said as we drank hot tea from thick white mugs and ate dripping egg and bacon butties in a steaming transport café close to Waterloo Station.

"You sound just like him," I muttered through the egg and bread.

"Who?"

"Warren."

"Won't she have left the country?"

"No. Whoever has got their eye on her won't let her leave. Anyway, where can she go? Everyone wants her."

"What do they know?"

"Ah. . . they know about the program, that's for sure. Well, the Stock Exchange's surveillance team does. The police have got the photographs. The SE tie her in with me. They tie me in with the program and the hacker. The surveillance team will have tapes of conversations and a database of all the transactions she and Eddie have made. But I know the codeword she and Eddie used, and I know which venture capital fund has their money and where. I don't think the authorities do but it won't take them long to find out."

"So why don't you just tell the police."

Nick waited for me to wipe the yolk from my chin before offering me a cigarette. I shook my head.

"I'm trying to give up."

"How are you going to do that?" Nick said with a smile. He flicked his Fix lighter open, rubbing his thumb down it a few times until a blue and yellow flame spurted up.

"I'm giving everything up."

"Everything?" he questioned looking wickedly at me from under his dark brows.

"Everything," I replied, with a smile.

"Liar."

I laughed and took a sip of scalding tea.

"You haven't answered me," he said.

It wasn't that he lacked intelligence; he had that. He lacked deviousness, real back-alley in-and-out deviousness. Nick took nice posed photographs in studios. It was when he was out and about tracking a news story that he really had to use his head. He had to be in the right place to get the right shot, to anticipate the event. It was hard, harder than my job, because I had time to think about what I'd seen and heard, mull it over and then write it. If Nick's camera was a fraction too slow, he'd have missed the news. My job was different. I had to get behind those faces for the truth, work on them, think like them; and to do that I had to be as tricky as a five-headed snake.

"Let's just say not everyone is pulling together on this one. I might talk to Falk. He's sound, I think, but it's that cold fish, Macnemie, I'm worried about. I don't think Falk has been 'fully briefed' – know what I mean?

"You see, what we know as the UK financial services industry regulates *itself* in the first instant. There's the Securities and Investment Board, but that's not even a government watchdog; it's a quango with delegated statutory powers. The Bank of England, patron of the Stock Exchange, helps the Department of Trade and Industry choose the SIB chairman, and the DTI gets to agree on the Bank's choice of the rest of the board. It's a really a case of inmates as wardens, the lunatics taking over the asylum. The US Securities and Exchange Commission can prosecute. The SIB can only investigate, seize documents and all that. The really serious stuff – including the prosecutions – gets handled by the DTI inspectors, privately or publicly. Crimes are also passed to the Director of Public Prosecutions, but he's hardly an active persecutor of City fraudsters. No, I reckon the Stock Exchange is going to want to sweep up its own yard first, before inviting in the neighbours."

As I saw it, Eddie had a choice. He could run for it or stay and strike a deal: he takes the money and the rap for a securities misdemeanour on Kirren Ventures, and no more is said about subliminal programs. The SEC would want to trash him, too, because he worked for a US securities house, but he could handle that if the can was lined with dollar bills.

Nick looked depressed. "What about the guys that did over your flat, my flat. Tried to beat ten kinds of crap out of you?"

I shrugged. "Look, I don't know. The hacking thing could turn nasty. I really don't know, but I've got a feeling

Eddie or Fisher, or both, if she's nice about it, will swing it. They'll walk with a hefty fine and a suspended jail sentence. The DTI will drive the accused through the streets in an open cart and make a show of hurling them into the void, into that awful darkness outside the golden square."

"That's unbelievable. It can't happen, can it?"

"A scandal like this. . . well it could change everything, Nick. The last thing the Stock Exchange or the SIB want is the DTI picking over the flesh of this one. Apart from the implications for the 24-hour global electronic marketplace, there's the City's power to regulate itself, something it's fought tooth and nail for. It's all about information, the the power of information, the selling of the network.

"I'll give you an example. Back in the Seventies, the top merchant banks tried to break the monopoly of the Stock Exchange in securities trading with a computerised trading system of their own. But the Bank of England killed it stone dead by handing the Stock Exchange the monopoly in gilts dealing. The system was crap anyway, but what I'm trying to say is that the Stock Exchange hasn't got a God-given right to monopolise an electronic marketplace. It doesn't own the floor anymore. Reuters and the rest are already competing with it. It can't afford to tell the world that its information system isn't secure, because that's all there is now: information. So I have to be very careful – selective. You see, I might want to divorce Eddie, but I don't want him dead. I want him alive and trading. I want them to know he wants to trade."

Nick stubbed out his cigarette in the little red metal ashtray on the table.

"Don't be daft. No one would actually kill him, would they?"

"Fisher would, and the authorities just might. It has been known. People falling out of windows, prodded with poisonous umbrellas, gassed in their cars, shot in a field. There's a lot at stake here. We're talking about money, remember – confidence in it, in the system. We saw what panic could do last week. Now tell all those people it was done on purpose and how."

Nick raised his eyebrows and nodded. Then he snatched up the photograph that I had laid on the table between us and flicked at Warren's head.

"What about this guy Warren? Where does he come in?"

I shrugged and we carried on sipping our tea in silence.

"Want another?" he asked eventually.

"No, I've got to go. Let's split this," I said, digging in my purse while he made noises about paying.

"Look. . ." he said, softly, taking my hand. I drew it away.

"No," I said firmly.

"Can I help?" he replied, trying to look into my eyes.

"You have done, already. I don't need you this time. It's sweet of you, but I think we have photographs of everyone now, don't you?"

Nick looked away, then back, and laughed.

"You bitch," he said, shaking his head.

I made a couple of calls before we went back to the office. Max looked suspiciously at us from behind his terminal, but he just waved us through. Then he called out.

"Oh, Nick. . . Mai called. Marianne can't make it tomorrow. Sorry, et cetera, et cetera. . ."

Nick waved a hand at Max and moved on. By the time we got upstairs he was twitching to leave again.

"Look, I've got to go. I need to see my flat, clear up some more stuff. . .Uh, look, I think you ought to call the police. . .really. Let them sort this out. . ."

"I already have done," I said gently. "You OK? Bad news?"

"Nah. – My kid, Marianne. . .we try to see each other Sundays. It doesn't always happen. It's OK," he replied, bending down to rummage in his case.

"Will you be back here tonight?" I asked, a little embarrassed by his obvious disappointment. It made me feel unjustifiably guilty too.

"Could be, why?"

"Just in case I need to call?"

"OK."

I needed some sleep before Eddie called that evening, so I left Nick sadly sorting out his world in a briefcase.

Eddie called at 7.00 pm. "It's set up," he said. "You do your thing."

He picked me up at 8.30pm in a black Fiat Uno Turbo which he directed rapidly through the West End traffic, east towards Wapping High Street.

"Did he turn up?" I asked as we weaved in and out.

"Sure. But are you sure he's going to help? You trust him?"

"No, but Falk's OK," I said confidently.

"Great," he said, ramming his hand on the gear-stick and putting his foot down.

Fisher turned up at 9.30pm on the dot. We heard the lift and I took my position by the large window from where I could see the lights of Bermondsey and Rotherhithe south across the water.

She was wearing soft black leather trousers and a red Chanel-style cashmere jacket. Her auburn hair was loose, but brushed back off her tense white face.

"What's *she* doing here?" were her first ill-humoured words.

"She's my wife. She can be here," Eddie replied coolly, shutting the door with a click.

She dealt me a poisonous look and turned back to Eddie. "Let's go."

I tried not to look too uncomfortable.

"I thought we could discuss the deal here. We agreed. I don't want any funny business, Kay," Eddie replied, hardening his voice.

"Our mutual friend says no," she responded with a heavy belt of sarcasm. "Our mutual friend suggests we talk out in the open where we won't be . . . how shall I put it, monitored?"

Eddie looked at me. I got up.

"I'll follow. I'm just going to the toilet."

I walked from the spacious lounge into a narrow corridor, tapping the door of the third bedroom lightly as I went. Falk held the door ajar. I shook my head, beckoned with my hand and thumbed my way out before stepping into the bathroom. It was OK, I thought, as I looked into the large square mirror theatrically lit by ten bright little bulbs on each side. Get them all together. Just hope Falk gets on his bike.

Fisher took the wheel of a grey BMW, with Eddie in the passenger seat and me in the back. The seats were leather, the windows smoky. Her rich perfume clung to the air like honey on a spoon. She didn't bother to show off the quadrophonic sound system on our silent journey, and there was no rain. It was a clear autumnal sky, with the creamy round moon up high like a puffball. I could see Fisher's pale kitten eye checking the mirrors, checking me. Her eyelashes were softly curled and dark with mascara. I couldn't look behind, but I hoped that dipped beam reflected in the rear-view mirror was our man. She drove fast through the turns and back doubles. I hung queasily on to the strap. She wasn't taking any chances this time.

"Where in hell are we?" Eddie demanded, as we drove off the dual carriageway that fed the Blackwall Tunnel. Fisher slowed up in a large ill-lit car park as big as a football pitch, and hauled up the handbrake. We were close to some old oast-houses and I could smell the stagnant water of a canal.

"Tesco's," I said wearily. "I used to live near here. Apparently I still do. . ."

"Get out. Let's talk," Fisher ordered viciously. I could tell she found my proximity upsetting.

"Aw, c'mon, Kay, what is this?" Eddie protested. She didn't reply and we followed her to a darker corner of the supermarket car park, nearer to the canal bridge. The sound of big wheels rumbled relentlessly behind us. We gathered together in a tight triangle, the crisp breeze that had buffeted us by the river now blowing languidly around us like the breath of a spent runner.

"Where's our mutual friend?" I inquired innocently. "Where is your YTS hit squad?"

Fisher's glance was hostile. Eddie was also clearly annoyed.

"Let's talk," he said softly to her, as if I was the hobnail-booted interloper.

"OK, what's the plan?" she demanded. I looked around. Warren had to be there somewhere. He was watching, I knew he was. As I squinted into dark corners, I hoped Falk had crept into one of them. He had to get closer. I had a wire but I hadn't bargained for this. I wanted the strong overweight arm of the law close by.

"We trade," said Eddie

"Who with?"

"The Exchange. We take a bath for dealing out of line. We swallow the fine and the sentence. We say nothing about the hack. You take your pretty boy off into the sunset."

"What about the fund?" Fisher said bitterly, as if she already knew the answer.

"We share it, as agreed, and I forgive and forget about your deal with him. We can survive this if we stick together, Kay." Eddie was talking tough, but with the gentlest touch.

"I don't want her in." She twisted her head in my direction. I was listening but the rest of my senses were straining to every rustle and crackle, every muffled scrape that could be a footstep.

"She ain't in. OK? She gets nothing. All she wants is out of the trap you set her."

"No." Fisher was being ungenerous and obstinate.

"Look, Kay, I know you double-crossed me. I know you want me out. Well, I want out. I'll take Lifestyle and what I made, and take a walk. But we've got to come in from the cold on this one. They know. They know she knows as much as us. We're not going to get away with it all. Let's just take some. Hell, it's enough, dammit!"

"But it's not, not now," she said coldly. "I'm tired of this silly little game. The fund is worth a fraction of what we could have made. Frankly, it's worth fuck all. We lost forty million dollars in six hours because of that "BUY" message. I didn't double-cross you, you blasted idiot. He did. He screwed us both. He's got the fucking lot. . . and it's that cow's fault."

She lunged at me with her newly-grown nails curled and

raking at my face. I swung away and, as Eddie caught her tiny wrist in his fist, two men stepped up from the bridge. They needed no introduction.

"OK," said Eddie, holding tightly to Fisher's wrist. "So the gang's all here. Be very, very careful now. Let's stay cool."

"Get her!" Fisher hissed, but I was already running back across the wide expanse of tarmac towards where I hoped Falk would be. I should have known: once all the crooks got together, the odd one out would be me.

"Where was our mutual friend?" my own question came back to terrorise me as I started running for my life.

I ran like a rabbit, dodging and swerving across open land, a moving target looking for scant cover in a wasteland. The ground I'd thought was flat was an incline, my arms pumped up and down as my lungs squeezed tighter and tighter on the air that I struggled to inhale. I was out of condition. It was a long time since I had run and jumped with the first seven, thrown a rounders ball or sprinted 200 yards for a certificate with my name in italics and a little silver cup. No more cigarettes, no more drink, I swore to God. There was a dull crack on the ground to my left: my first experience of real gunfire.

I knew that if I looked back I would stumble. My head was falling back and rolling from side to side. Any commentator would have said I was suffering – this athlete is in trouble – but I kept going, hoping my skinny legs would keep me moving forwards, stretching out towards the road. At least I knew the terrain. If I went to the right, there would be the flyover, and a roundabout sucking in a continuous stream of cars which rolled around and flicked out at speed like balls on a pinball machine. They'd never stop, but if I could get across there was a pub to the left.

The slap of leather shoes behind me and the jangle of pocket change pressed more adrenaline into my veins, but my effort was beginning to collapse. There were more shots behind me and I ran on in the bright moonlight, chased by my own shadow and the thudding beat of one pair of fast, gaining footsteps.

I didn't see the wire shopping trolley, half in and half out of the road. It caught my leg and I spun round to face my pursuer. He looked greyer in the moonlight but there was no mistaking his face. It was Warren. I desperately tried to gain my balance, to turn and run, but he caught his arm around my waist and whipped me back, dragging me into shadows.

"You bastard," I gasped. "You bastard."

We stood breathing hard and painfully against each other for at least five minutes. My recovery was made less easy by Warren's damp cold hand clamped hard across my mouth.

"Listen to me. Listen to me," he whispered finally, his lips close behind my ear. "You're the one everyone wants. Kay Fisher has already done a deal with Macnemie. You're the one that wants to run the story. Everyone has already made their deals. Everyone. . .even your paper. There is just you. But I've got the money, understand? I'm the man. You got a choice."

My legs came up off the floor and I felt myself dropping backwards over a wall. Warren pulled me down some stairs and I could see moonlight on water. I knew this towpath. You could walk along it to the Lea Valley in the north-east of London without ever having to cross a road, and to the south there was Bow Creek and the Thames.

I heard the sound of a fast car on the road above. Then I heard a low, even voice and saw the top of Falks's straw-coloured head.

"All right, lads? Steady now. Where's the party?"

"Don't say a word. Nuffin', right?" Warren whispered in my ear.

I nodded and he released his hand from my mouth, while his arm drew me into the shadows by the damp wall.

"Wait till you hear him come back. Then go up. He'll have rounded them up. You'll be OK now."

"No," I said. "I'll make my own way to Bishopsgate. Take a cab maybe?"

He'd taken a risk being there, coming back for me. I could only see his eyes and his white teeth. He was smiling broadly. Mine own familiar friend, the shark, had had his dinner, but what did he expect now?

"It's worked out pretty good. . . almost perfect. Almost," he said.

I didn't answer him. I didn't like him anymore, not a bit. But it pleased me to know that he loved me, because I knew how that could hurt. Loving someone who was never there, who never called, whom you could never see again and you always wondered what they were doing now, and whether they ever thought of you, and as you racked yourself with their image wrapped close in the arms of another, you foolishly hoped that perhaps they were unsatisfied because it wasn't you. Money could answer everything, but it could never answer that.

CHAPTER FIFTEEN

THERE WAS A LIGHT STENCH of rotting rubbish in the damp night air as we stepped into the lift in the tenement where I had lived. The old hip-hop had been sprayed over again with a glowing man. We travelled to the sixth floor in the company of a baggy, paper-filled Guy Fawkes, lolling sideways with a plastic Margaret Thatcher mask strapped to its turnip head. Around its neck was a placard saying "Peny for the guy."

There was a lot of noise from two of the other flats on the landing. Loud music. Saturday night was crashing into Sunday morning. I rummaged in my bag for the keys which Warren had given me, unlocked the door and pushed it open. I had to step back out again to check the number: 601.

It smelled of fresh paint. The doors and windows had been painted a brilliant white, the walls in light grey. Deep blue velvet curtains hung from the windows. The rooms were laid wall-to-wall with a pure wool navy carpet flecked with a light peach-coloured dots. There was no furniture. There was no lampshade. Warren's computer had gone, and all his grey metal boxes of communications equipment. There were no boxes of software. There were no shelves.

The bedroom had been changed. There was a new unmade bed, two new pillows and a duvet. There was some white linen and a peach-coloured duvet cover folded neatly at the end of the bed. The peach velvet curtains were drawn together.

A light wood wardrobe, dressing table and chair furnished the room.

I sat carefully on the chair and gently pulled open a drawer. It was filled with silk underwear, in grey and black. No labels, all new. Another drawer revealed stockings and tights, another peach satin pyjamas, some cotton shirts, two cashmere sweaters – one black, one camel. In the wardrobe hung an MA1 flying jacket and a pair of red-label 501s. There were two dresses – one black, one red; and two skirts – one black, one grey; two pairs of black shoes – a pair with heels from Russell and Bromley and a pair of Doctor Martins. Everything was in my size, everything was new.

"Are you OK?" said Falk, filling the doorway with his bulk.

"Yeah, yeah," I said quietly. He stood gently aside as I moved past him into the bathroom. It had been completely refurbished. There was a new white suite, a white oval mirror, a shower and a navy curtain. The floor was carpeted in peach, and the new soft towels matched the carpet.

To my relief the kitchen was the same as it had been.

"He didn't have time for this," I said to myself. "He just didn't have time for this."

Warren had found time to change the crockery and cutlery. Two bottles of wine, a pizza, a loaf of bread, some butter and some cheese were in the fridge. There were jars of instant coffee, tea and marmalade in a cupboard.

"Look, if you're not up to this. . ." Falk offered as I stood staring out of the kitchen window. I could see the light of the NatWest tower better from up there. The whole city twinkled before me like a field of broken glass, and the dark window reflected my own wan face.

"I'm OK. I'm just really tired now," I said, pulling down the blind.

"I'm sorry." His voice was heavy and low.

"What for?" I said, not turning around but reaching instead for the coffee jar. I carried on putting coffee in the cups and filling the kettle with water. It boiled quickly and we sat together at the kitchen table. His words irritated me. I couldn't stand being pitied, being judged and analysed by men who got so close to me that I was out of focus. Yet it always happened. How come it always happened?

"I don't work hard at it. It just sort of comes to me in a flash of morbidity," I said ruefully.

"Yes," he replied as if he understood, pushing his glasses up his nose with his pudgy fingers.

"You won't find him, you know," I said expressionlessly. "He's gone. He'll have erased everything. He's good, very good." I stopped and Falk just carried on listening to the emptiness. Then he spoke in that soft reasonable voice of his.

"The Sundays already had the story. It was sewn up and released to them before your husband picked you up. City rocked by securities scandal, senior staff dismissed, and all that. No one will run your story. There is no proof anymore. Not about your cousin or about the crash. I'm sorry I wasn't there, but I think you can count yourself lucky Graham was." Falk looked a little embarrassed.

"Who was Macnemie? He wasn't from the Stock Exchanges, surely?"

He shook his huge head, and pointed upstairs.

"They tried to kill me."

"So you say."

"With a gun."

Falk came a little closer.

"It's no good. I can't do a thing about any of it. They all walk, that's the deal, albeit with a label round their necks saying unclean, but they walk. Look. . . just keep the money and forget it."

"No," I said bitterly, "I'll never forget this. Could you?"

"No. It's been an education, that's for sure. The money – it's yours, fair and square. OK, so you didn't open the account, didn't put up the margin, but it's still yours."

"Oh yeah, a small donation for the needy from a real pal," I replied.

"Well, if what you say is true, he was one. . . in the end," Falk replied putting his ruby lips to the hot coffee cup and sipping gently. "He saved your life, made sure you got some money out of it, did up this place for you, and taught them, including his erstwhile mistress, a little lesson to boot, for messing you about. . . . We'd certainly like to interview him of course."

"So would I, D.I. Falk, so would I."

Of course, we never did. I never saw Warren Graham again. The story of Kirren Ventures ran for weeks in the nationals and Sundays. It made the *Wall Street Journal* and the *Washington Post* when the SEC investigated Eddie's and Fisher's activities at Broadwick & Klein. They both consented to a permanent injunction preventing them from violating US or UK security laws in the future. Fisher was fined $300,000, Eddie $100,000, and they both got twelve-month suspended sentences – no community service. The pundits thought that it showed that the authorities were kicking City fraudsters at last.

Warren had been right, though: everyone had taken a cut when the horse-trading had begun, everyone who knew – everyone, it seemed, except Falk and me. And Warren had made sure I was OK, so that just left Falk buying his suits from Burton's.

Eddie and I are divorced, but I didn't name Celia. He runs Lifestyle Software out of Orange County. His biggest customers are multi-national corporations who want to use this program and its message to instil the work ethic in their employees. Fisher joined the Unification Church.

Charlie got the sack, but paid his debts, and I kept the £75,000 but never wrote my story. I resigned. Mary Stow got my job. Falk and I go out to dinner sometimes, and I think he's losing weight.

LINES AND SHADOWS

Joseph Wambaugh

'The best book yet'
New York Times Book Review

The team: the Border Alien Robbery Force. Ten tough men hailed as the last of the gunslingers. The mission: to stalk the vicious bandits who rob, rape and murder illegal aliens trying to cross the Mexican border. LINES AND SHADOWS is a true wild west police story you'll never forget.

'Written in Wambaugh's most compelling, exciting prose'
Publishers Weekly

'Brilliantly written, hilariously funny'
Times Literary Supplement

FUTURA PUBLICATIONS
NON-FICTION
0 7088 2645 8

TOURIST SEASON

Carl Hiaasen

The only trace of the first victim was his fez washed up on the Miami beach. The second victim, the head of the city's chamber of commerce, was found dead with a toy rubber alligator lodged in his throat. And that was just the beginning . . .

Now Brian Keys, reporter turned private eye, must move from muckraking to murder as he strives to uncover a bizarre conspiracy that involves football players, politicians, policemen, business tycoons and beauty queens with a group of crazed fanatics and a very hungry crocodile.

'Wonderful . . . lively . . . fun . . . A remarkable example of what talented writers are doing these days with the mystery novel.'
New York Times Book Review

'One of the most exciting novels of the season . . . kept me riveted to the end!'
Chicago Tribune

'I can't remember another novel which combines violence and comedy so successfully.'
John D. Macdonald

FUTURA PUBLICATIONS
FICTION/CRIME
0 7088 3388 8

FATHERS' LAW

D. W. Smith

'First-rate' *Sunday Times*

Harry Fathers – overworked Detective Chief Inspector at
Scotland Yard – is furious. His assignment in New York
investigating the disappearance of Michael Sampson, a
British academic, is most inconvenient.

But the reluctant Fathers soon becomes intrigued by his
off-beat investigation. Whitehall has deliberately misled
him. The FBI are more deeply involved than they care to
admit. Sampson's lover Rosemary is convinced his
disappearance was forced – and probably fatal.

Fathers soon finds himself immersed in the deadly and
murky world of satellite spies and international defence.
And then he finds that the FBI and the mandarins in
Whitehall are going to cover up his findings . . .

A gripping and accomplished thriller, and the first in a
series about Harry Fathers.

FUTURA PUBLICATIONS
FICTION/CRIME
0 7088 3443 4

All Futura Books are available at your bookshop or
newsagent, or can be ordered from the following address:
Futura Books, Cash Sales Department,
P.O. Box 11, Falmouth, Cornwall TR10 9EN.

Please send cheque or postal order (no currency), and
allow 60p for postage and packing for the first book
plus 25p for the second book and 15p for each additional
book ordered up to a maximum charge of £1.90 in U.K.

B.F.P.O. customers please allow 60p for
the first book, 25p for the second book plus 15p per
copy for the next 7 books, thereafter 9p per book

Overseas customers, including Eire, please allow £1.25
for postage and packing for the first book, 75p for the
second book and 28p for each subsequent title ordered.